49 WAYS TO THINK YOURSELF WELL

JAN ALCOE AND EMILY GAJEWSKI

49 WAYS TO
THINK
YOURSELF WELL

Mind science in practice, one step at a time

JAN ALCOE AND EMILY GAJEWSKI

First published in Great Britain in 2013 by Step Beach Press Ltd, Brighton

A CIP catalogue record for this title is available from the British Library.

ISBN 978-1-908779-05-2

Photograph credits

Pp 12, 15, 24, 33, 50, 64, 140 Jessica Atkinson and Stephanie Dale,
pp 36,58, 63, 86, 93, 117, 126, 137, 138 Dan Betts, p82 Judi Dettmar,
p133 Kevin Dooley, p45 Tony Fischer, p53 Horia Varlan,
p90 Manuel Silveira Ramos, p102 ButterflySha

Series editor Jan Alcoe

Edited by Jo Hathaway

Typeset in Brighton, UK by Keren Turner at Katch Creative

Cover design by Keren Turner at Katch Creative

Printed and bound by Star Standard Industries, Singapore

Step Beach Press Ltd, 28 Osborne Villas, Hove, East Sussex BN3 2RE

www.stepbeachpress.co.uk

*For our children, who teach us daily
about wise living and well-being*

Acknowledgements

In recognition of the research into emotional well-being
by the Human Givens Institute, UK, and the inspiration we
have had from the teaching of Ivan Tyrrell and Joe Griffin
(Human Givens Institute), Mark Tyrrell (Uncommon Knowledge),
and Jill Wootton (Within Sight).

We would also like to acknowledge the many people we
have been privileged to work with therapeutically,
and what they have taught us about the power of
the mind and the resilience of the human spirit.

49 Ways to Well-being Series

If you have selected this book, you may be looking for practical ways of improving your well-being. If you are a health and well-being practitioner or therapist, you may be helping your clients to improve theirs by encouraging them to practise some of the approaches it is based on. Well-being is a subjective state of 'feeling good' which has physical, mental, emotional and even spiritual dimensions.

Because these dimensions overlap and interact, it is possible to improve well-being by making positive changes in any one of them. For example, taking up regular exercise (a focus on physical well-being) may improve concentration (mental well-being), happiness (emotional well-being) and sense of purpose (spiritual well-being). This series of well-being books is designed to provide a variety of routes to recovering, sustaining, protecting and enhancing well-being, depending on your interests and motivations. While some emphasise psychological techniques, others are based on physical movement, nutrition, journaling and many other approaches.

Each book in the series provides 49 practical ways of improving well-being, based on a particular therapeutic approach and written by an expert in that field. Based on tried and tested approaches, each title offers the user a rich source of tools for well-being. Some of these can be used effectively for improving general resilience; others are particularly helpful for specific problems or issues you may be dealing with, for example, recovering from illness, improving relaxation and sleep, or boosting motivation and self-confidence.

Enjoy dipping into any *49 Ways* book and selecting ones which catch your interest or help you to meet a need at a particular time. We have deliberately included many different ideas for practice, knowing that some will be more appropriate at different times, in different situations and with different individuals. You may find certain approaches so helpful or enjoyable that you build them into everyday living, as part of your own well-being strategy.

Having explored one book, you may be interested in using some of the other titles to add to your well-being 'toolbox', learning how to approach your well-being via a number of different therapeutic routes.

For more information about the series, including current and forthcoming titles, visit **www.stepbeachpress.co.uk/well-being**

CONTENTS

1 2 3 4 5 6 7 8
9 10 11 12 13 14
15 16 17 18 19
20 21 22 23 24
25 26 27 28 29
30 31 32 33 34
35 36 37 38 39
40 41 42 43 44
45 46 47 48 49

INTRODUCTION

Welcome to *49 Ways to Think Yourself Well*. As you dip into this guide, you will be learning about and using a wide range of ideas and techniques to improve your well-being, drawn from the broad field of contemporary psychology, including cognitive behaviour therapy, cognitive mindfulness, occupational therapy, hypnotherapy, Human Givens therapy, positive psychology, compassion-focused therapy and neuro-linguistic programming (NLP). All these approaches have evolved from research into our innate mental resources and the strong links between our thinking, emotions and behaviour. This guide will steer you around the pitfalls of negative thinking, harmful emotions and stress-led behaviours which will impair your physical and mental well-being. You can then learn how to use your own mental resources in positive ways to meet your needs, whether to improve your physical health, boost your confidence or motivation, keep calm in the face of challenge, improve your relationships or reach peak performance.

While you can start using the ideas and activities in this book in any order, we would encourage you to begin with some fundamentals, which we have organised into Chapter 1. These are designed to calm, relax and focus you. Many of the techniques introduced in this book work most effectively when you are in a relaxed state because your mind is then best able to problem solve, see things in perspective, and access a whole host of unconscious resources which you may not even know are there! You may want to begin by discovering what it is like to be deeply relaxed on a regular basis, and how this can help you to tackle issues you might want to address. If a particular activity or technique requires that you begin by relaxing, you will be pointed to one of these preliminary exercises first. You can also practise deep relaxation techniques by accessing the free audio downloads which accompany this book, on the Step Beach website **www.stepbeachpress.co.uk/well-being**.

GLOSSARY

There is a glossary at the back of this book which explains some of the terms used in more detail. Any words that appear in the glossary have an asterisk next to them in the text, like this*.

USEFUL RESOURCES

Finally, we have listed some useful resources, should you wish to explore any of the themes or psychological approaches in more depth.

A NOTE OF WARNING

This guide is not intended to replace seeking medical or professional help for significant physical, emotional or mental problems. We would suggest that this is essential if you are experiencing any of the following:

- Undiagnosed pain, physical symptoms or sleep problems
- Symptoms of depression, such as loss of motivation, loss of appetite, changes in sleeping habits, persistent negative thinking
- High levels of anxiety or anger or recurring panic attacks
- Substance misuse or self-harming behaviours
- Social isolation due to severe lack of confidence or self-esteem
- Persistent relationship difficulties.

Each numbered 'way' provides a significant route to recovering, preserving or enhancing your well-being. It will usually include:

- underpinning theory, evidence or information on a particular issue and helpful approaches
- a **'Tip'** for making an immediate, small change in how you think or feel
- a **'Try this'**, longer activity to put theory into practice
- numbered references to support factual information (full details of which can be found at the back of the book)
- a **'See also'** which suggests other, numbered 'ways' which you may find it helpful to look at.

We have organised the *49 Ways* into categories of common challenges and needs which we may come across in our lives.

A GUIDE TO THE CHAPTERS

Chapter 1: Lay the Foundations for Well-being: Some mind science basics

This chapter helps you to lay down some important foundation stones for well-being based on the science of the mind. It introduces an evidence-based list of emotional needs which are essential to well-being and happiness. You can rate how well you are getting those needs met and begin to plan some positive changes. You will learn about the importance of 'switching off' the body's 'fight-or-flight' or stress response* when it is not needed, thus avoiding many stress-related health problems. You can try some effective techniques for deep relaxation based on mindfulness and visualisation. You can begin to identify and connect with internal and external resources which you can draw on to support your

well-being, particularly in challenging times. All these practices underpin the contents of this book. Learning to use them will enable you to harness the power of your mind to enhance well-being on many levels.

Two free audio downloads are available to support this chapter at **www.stepbeachpress.co.uk**

Chapter 2: Deal with Stress, Anxiety, Panic and Worry

The stress response can be triggered by our fears, anxiety and worry and can sometimes lead us into a full-blown panic attack. This chapter will help you to avoid unnecessary stress in your life by concentrating on what you *can* change. You will learn how to evoke a sense of calm in stressful situations, and how to handle or avoid panic attacks to help you stay in control of your life. You can practise techniques for reducing the amount of time spent worrying and some emergency strategies for distracting yourself away from fear, anxiety and worry. Reducing your response to stress in these ways will enhance your well-being and put you back in control of your life.

Two free audio downloads are available to support this chapter on **www.stepbeachpress.co.uk**

Chapter 3: Control Negative Thinking and Avoid Depression

How we think is closely linked to how we feel and how we then act in our lives. We can sometimes believe that we *are* our thoughts and this can lead us into a state of hopelessness and helplessness. Negative thinking can trigger the stress response and is at the heart of depression. This chapter will help you to separate yourself from your thoughts, so that you can be objective about their content. You can learn about common errors of thinking so that you can guard against them. It is important to challenge negative thoughts and consciously change them, and there are several techniques included for doing just this. Finally, we cover the importance of understanding the cycle of depression which can be triggered by constant negative thinking, called rumination. Learning to avoid this pattern of thinking will help to ensure that you continue experiencing motivation and pleasure in life.

Chapter 4: Reduce Anger

Uncontrolled rage and anger are extremely destructive to our health, relationships, property and community. Our daily lives can often include so little 'down time' that stress levels creep up and up to the point where we 'boil over'. If you are someone with trauma or unresolved emotional difficulties from the past, you are also more likely to be at the mercy of uncontrolled anger. Whilst feeling angry

at injustice or wrongdoing in the world can spur us forward to do something productive, uncontrolled outbursts of anger lead only downwards and, at their worst, can be life-threatening.

This chapter explains what is going on in the brain when anger starts to rise and what we can do to prevent this happening. You can learn strategies to nip it in the bud so that you just don't get to boiling point, and how to review and change how you react in anger-provoking situations. This will help you to keep your rational mind in charge of your life so you can live your life how you would like to, more of the time.

Chapter 5: Improve Physical Health and Sleep

There is a growing body of research which demonstrates the interconnections between the brain, behaviour, immunity and health. For example, how we use our minds, including our thoughts, expectations and how we interpret life's events, can greatly impact upon our body's cellular activity and immunity and a whole host of physiological functions (12). This chapter will help you learn ways of creating an image of wellness and reducing the harmful effects of stress by 'self-soothing'. Pain has a strong psychological element, so you can practise ways of reducing pain and discomfort. You can also foster positive expectations about medical treatment and your body's ability to heal.

Sleep is often disturbed by stress and we develop unhelpful patterns of behaviour which can make it difficult to get deep rest at night. This chapter also includes tips on sleep hygiene and ways of changing thoughts and feelings around sleep. Finally, you can learn how to use the natural dream state to get off to a good night's sleep.

Chapter 6: Set Goals and Boost Your Motivation

How often have you felt the frustration of promising yourself that you *will* make a change, whether starting a new routine or achieving something important to you, only to find yourself a few months down the line having not achieved those things, *again*? Our basic human need to feel in control of our lives, to learn and feel challenged, and have a sense of achievement are all assaulted by this sense of failure. If it is continually repeated, life can start to feel 'stuck', empty or even meaningless. It is for this important reason that we have devoted this chapter to achieving goals. In this chapter you will find an opportunity to stand back and refocus on what is important in your life. You can then learn how to set realistic and achievable goals and, most importantly, how to motivate yourself to achieve them. Rather than floating aimlessly through life, you will have gained some practical skills to begin moving in just the right direction for you.

Chapter 7: Enhance Your Assertiveness, Self-esteem and Confidence

There is a wealth of self-help material available for people who feel lacking in self-esteem and confidence, which is perhaps an indication of what a common complaint this is. Trying to feel better about ourselves can prompt us to go down all sorts of unhelpful avenues and sometimes this can lead to unhealthy or destructive habits, which we address in Chapter 9. This chapter will help you take effective steps to becoming a more confident person, starting by cultivating a sense of achievement, which meets an important emotional need in all of us. It goes on to distil some of the best, evidence-based techniques

and tools around, providing a practical guide to feeling better about yourself and behaving more assertively. Acting confidently, setting boundaries and saying what you mean may feel unfamiliar and challenging. Don't worry, there are tips along the way that will help you take the plunge and then follow easy steps to becoming a more confident person.

Chapter 8: Improve Communication and Relationships

Relationships are at the heart of so much of what we do in all areas of our life – work, family and leisure. This chapter will help you to hone your skills of communication and relationship building. It begins by introducing theoretical and practical techniques for developing rapport with other people, so that you can better understand how they feel and learn how to see their point of view. You can then look at some of the basic differences in the way in which men and women's brains function, which can make a big, positive difference when trying to negotiate with the opposite sex!

You can learn some effective ways for diffusing conflict in relationships, helping you to express feelings and move forward, rather than get locked into destructive patterns or arguments.

Finally, you can be on the look-out for relationship busters – the behaviours which may lead to conflict and melt-down. All of these approaches apply not only in intimate relationships but all relationships, with wider family members, colleagues and friends. By applying some of the ideas in practice, you can quickly feel freed and on the road to more constructive and helpful relationships in your life.

Chapter 9: Change Unhelpful Patterns

When we are depleted, through excessive stress, traumatic events, loneliness or boredom, we all have the potential to reach out for destructive 'quick fixes'. The common ground with any habits is that they give an initial rush of chemical-induced pleasure within the brain. However, these positive feelings are shortly followed by feelings of regret, self-loathing and a dramatic drop in mood. We are all drawn to different habits; some of us will be drawn to an instant chemical hit from alcohol, caffeine, drugs or food; some of us will use the comfort or even pain of repetitive nail-biting or skin-picking/cutting to induce the soothing hit of natural endorphins; some of us may behave in ways that temporarily get our emotional need for attention or love met, such as shopping beyond our means or sex with strangers.

This chapter is focused on helping you 'take the high road' away from behaviours that you know are not working for you, however alluring they seem at the time.
It introduces a cycle of change which helps you to understand how to change and how to avoid the danger of self-sabotage. You will be able to identify your 'point of no return' in habitual behaviours and then move away from it. Finally, you can learn how to develop a more compassionate approach to your habit, which avoids the emotions of shame, blame and self-criticism which in themselves can be overwhelming. These models and techniques will help you to finally leave old habits behind and develop healthy and productive ways of coping with whatever life throws your way.

Chapter 10: Reach the Peak of Well-being

This final chapter helps you to put the icing onto the cake of well-being. Having explored how to use the mind to recover and improve well-being in a number of key ways, you can turn your attention to what you want and how you wish to feel as you move forwards in your life. You can use the power of the 'dreaming brain' to come up with new ideas and solutions. Much of this chapter is based on positive emotions as the key to building resilience and a lifetime of well-being. This includes how to develop positive emotions about the future, through cultivating optimism; positive emotions about the past, through gratitude and forgiveness; and positive emotions about the present, through using your signature strengths and enjoying the benefits of getting into flow*. Finally, we all have the opportunity of connecting our 'inner spirit' with our outer world, in terms of discovering a meaning and purpose in life. Paying attention to this need for connection can enhance our mental and physical health and completes the 'circle' of well-being. It enables us to give out and connect with others, to appreciate the beauty in the world and continue to be curious about our well-being and our very existence.

We hope you enjoy the journey.

1 2 3 4 5 6 7 8
9 10 11 12 13 14
15 16 17 18 19
20 21 22 23 24
25 26 27 28 29
30 31 32 33 34
35 36 37 38 39
40 41 42 43 44
45 46 47 48 49

Chapter 1

LAY THE FOUNDATIONS OF WELL-BEING: SOME MIND SCIENCE BASICS

This chapter helps you to lay down some important foundation stones for well-being based on the science of the mind. It introduces an evidence-based list of emotional needs which are essential to well-being and happiness. You can rate how well you are getting those needs met and begin to plan some positive changes. You will learn about the importance of 'switching off' the body's fight-or-flight or stress response when it is not needed, thus avoiding many stress-related health problems. You can try some effective techniques for deep relaxation based on mindfulness and visualisation. You can begin to identify and connect with internal and external resources which you can draw on to support your well-being, particularly in challenging times. All these practices underpin the contents of this book. Learning to use them will enable you to harness the power of your mind to enhance well-being on many levels.

Bulletproof your happiness

Meeting your emotional needs is essential for mental well-being.

There are hundreds of theories in psychology, all of which tell us they have the answers to our mental health. It's no wonder that many of us make confused and unsuccessful attempts at finding happiness and don't know where to turn for effective help.

Psychologists Joe Griffin and Ivan Tyrrell, founders of the Human Givens approach, were indeed puzzled by the plethora of psychological theories, particularly when compared with, for instance, biological theory, where there is one accepted model of how the human body works! With this confusion in mind, Griffin, Tyrrell and colleagues, set about a research project spanning many years, which put under the microscope all available psychological theory and techniques relating to mental well-being. Their aim was to draw together an evidence-based list from these many sources, one which could inform us as humans, what it is we need in our lives to be emotionally well. The resulting list of **emotional needs** (1) means that we no longer need to scrabble in the dark for what might make us happy. We now have a definitive checklist that we can refer to, noting where are scores are low and making adjustments in our lives accordingly.

Once you have rated your needs on the chart opposite, your task is to set yourself small goals, so you can begin shifting your scores higher. If this all seems rather daunting, see **WAY 28**: **Set realistic goals,** page 88, to help with the process!

NOTE
If any of your scores is under 3, they are likely to cause major stress in your life and may require some serious attention. If *many* of your scores are under 3, you may need to access professional help to prevent or deal with the emotional problems this can lead to.

Tip: Use this list particularly in times of change, eg. when you have moved house, changed job, or a relationship has ended. This is when we are particularly vulnerable, as our usual ways of getting our needs met may be compromised and we need to be creative about how to get them met in new ways.

Rating your emotional needs

Here is the list of emotional needs. Rate each one 1 to 10 to indicatehow well you feel you are getting that need met in your life at the moment, 1 = no, not at all, 10 = yes, totally.

	Not met	(please circle)	Met
Do you feel secure in all major areas of your life (such as your home, work, environment)?	1 2 3 4 5 6 7 8 9 10		
Do you feel you receive enough attention?	1 2 3 4 5 6 7 8 9 10		
Do you think you give other people enough attention?	1 2 3 4 5 6 7 8 9 10		
Do you feel in control of your life most of the time?	1 2 3 4 5 6 7 8 9 10		
Do you feel part of the wider community?	1 2 3 4 5 6 7 8 9 10		
Can you obtain privacy when you need to?	1 2 3 4 5 6 7 8 9 10		
Do you have an intimate relationship in your life (one where you are totally physically and emotionally accepted for who you are by at least one person, this could be a close friend)?	1 2 3 4 5 6 7 8 9 10		
Do you feel an emotional connection to others?	1 2 3 4 5 6 7 8 9 10		
Do you feel you have status that is acknowledged?	1 2 3 4 5 6 7 8 9 10		
Are you achieving things and competent in at least one major area of your life?	1 2 3 4 5 6 7 8 9 10		
Are you mentally and/or physically stretched in ways which give you a sense of meaning and purpose?	1 2 3 4 5 6 7 8 9 10		

Try this

WAY 2

Switch off the stress response

Learn to control one of the most basic and vital, underlying factors in our physical and mental health. By switching off the 'stress response' you can switch into relaxation and well-being.

Many of the chapters in this book are designed to help you prevent or counter what we call the stress response, often known as the 'fight-or-flight' response.

The human brain is hard-wired for survival. The amygdala* is part of the limbic system (the 'emotional brain') and is involved in many of our emotions and motivations, particularly those that are related to survival. Picture this as a burglar alarm in your house. While you are sleeping soundly, it constantly scans your environment for signs of danger, based on the sensory memories of your past experiences. If it recognises a threatening *sound* – a loud crash, *sight* – a looming shadow, *sensation* – crawling on the skin, or other sign of danger, it will activate. This will occur before you have had time to investigate whether a burglar has broken in or an overnight guest has decided to go downstairs for a drink of water!

When the alarm is activated powerful hormones, including adrenaline*, are released throughout the body, prompting a whole host of physiological changes to enable you to either fight or flee the danger. At this point, you may notice your heart palpitating, your body shaking and sweating and your breath coming in gasps, because your whole body has been mobilised for action. The survival mechanism is firmly based on 'live first and ask questions later'! Look at the diagram below.

THE STRESS RESPONSE IN ACTION

All these natural reactions are designed to divert energy to where it is needed to allow the body to go into survival mode

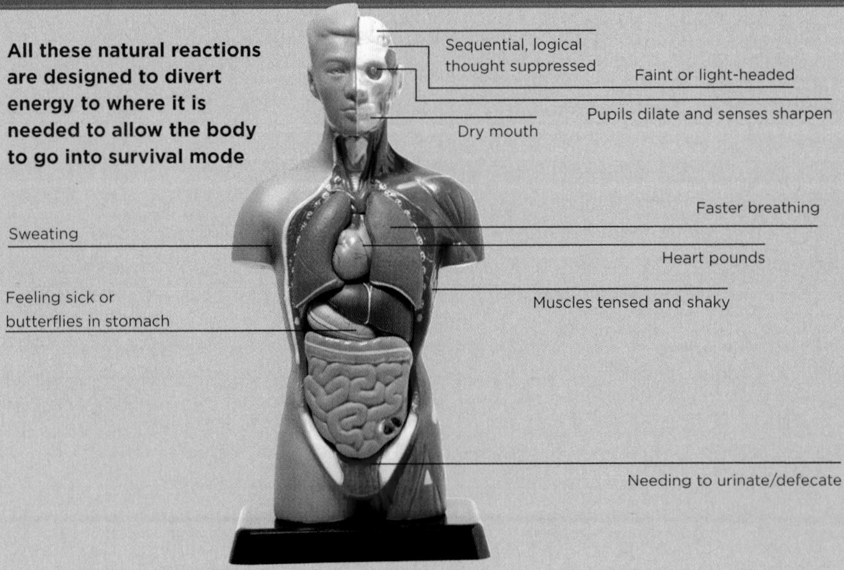

Sequential, logical thought suppressed

Faint or light-headed

Dry mouth

Pupils dilate and senses sharpen

Sweating

Faster breathing

Heart pounds

Feeling sick or butterflies in stomach

Muscles tensed and shaky

Needing to urinate/defecate

Unfortunately, the stress response can 'kick off' in a whole range of situations which we associate with fear but which are not, in themselves, life-threatening. For example, being faced with unreasonable work demands, giving a public performance, going into a hospital, or even when we just *imagine* ourselves in uncomfortable situations. The effects may impair our ability to control our body, for example, when we find ourselves shaking and sweating as we walk onto the stage to give a public talk.

Feeling stressed also means that we are more prey to our emotions, which operate from a 'threat or no-threat', 'good or bad' perspective. As the temperature rises, the emotional brain hijacks the higher neocortex (the 'thinking brain') which normally provides a more intelligent analysis of what is happening, following the initial danger trigger.

Consequently, we find ourselves unable to think clearly, keep things in perspective and make good judgments. For example, we may feel threatened in a meeting, and as our level of upset or anger increases, we are unable to make the fine distinctions we need to analyse and calmly influence opinions in the room.

When we are highly stressed, our anxiety may 'spill over' into a full-blown panic attack and we then experience more extreme physiological and mental effects (see **WAY 9: Don't panic!**, page 40).

If we do not allow our bodies to recover and re-balance, long-term stress hormones such as cortisol are released. In time, these can negatively affect our health, impairing our immune system, digestion, sleep and sex drive, or paving the way into depression, generalised anxiety or other mental difficulties (see **WAY 22: Break the link between stress and ill-health**, page 74).

We all need an optimum level of stress to be able to perform effectively when we need to, and sometimes we need the extra emotional arousal to give a big performance. However, being able to 'switch off' the stress response and 'switch on' the body's relaxation response (see page 26) avoids a build-up of stress hormones and is essential to our well-being – physically, mentally and emotionally. Stress and relaxation are two sides of the same coin, linked as they are to two different branches of the central nervous system. We can't experience feelings of relaxation and tension at the same time.

When we get stressed, we begin to breathe in short gasps. If we don't take any physical action, for example, running away or fighting for 'survival', then we take in more oxygen than we can use. As it is breathed out again, it takes carbon dioxide, essential to the absorption of oxygen by the body, with it. If too much carbon dioxide is lost from the body, we begin to experience the terrifying feeling of suffocating or choking, even though we are still breathing. One of the quickest ways to stop the stress response escalating (and stimulate the relaxation response) is to focus on a rhythm of breathing called 7/11 breathing.

NOTE
In a small number of cases, anxiety symptoms can be triggered by a physical condition, such as thyroid disorder or heart irregularity, or by a sudden change in consumption of caffeine, alcohol or tranquillisers.

7/11 breathing for instant relaxation

Breathe in (preferably through the nose) for a count of 7. Then breathe out more slowly to a count of 11. The longer out breath stimulates the body's natural relaxation response and quickly stops any panicky feelings. If you can't extend the out breath for 11, try breathing in to a count of 3, and out, more slowly, to a count of 5. Alternatively, just hold your breath while you continue counting and then take the next in breath.

Do this about 10 to 20 times, telling yourself that you are relaxing more with each breath.

Concentrate on the counting and notice how much less tense you feel in your body and mind.

This is also available as a free audio download on **www.stepbeachpress. co.uk**, along with a body scan relaxation.

Try this

SEE ALSO
- **WAY 3: Take a mindful approach to relaxation** (page 26)
- **WAY 8: Create an anchor for calm** (page 38)
- *Chapter 3*: *Control Negative Thinking and Avoid Depression* (pages 47 to 61)
- **WAY 17: Don't flip your lid! Stay cool and calm** (page 62)

Tip: If you feel your stress levels rising, focus the mind on a repetitive task for a minute or two, like counting backwards from 300 in 3s. This distracts away from thoughts which may be fuelling anxiety. Alternatively, take some vigorous exercise which uses the bodily changes which occur with the stress response for the purpose they were intended!

WAY 3

Take a mindful approach to relaxation

Learn how to prompt the body's relaxation response by practising mindfulness.

The relaxation response is the opposite of the stress response described in **WAY 2: Switch off the stress response**, page 22, and can be prompted by deep relaxation. There are untold benefits to practising relaxation on a regular basis. Not only does relaxation allow the body a chance to re-charge and repair, but it calms the mind so that we are more resourceful in how we handle situations, relate to others and make decisions. It is a foundation stone for well-being on all levels.

If you can create one part of this relaxation response, for example, slowing and deepening your breathing, then the chain of other responses will follow. We can harness the mind to lead the body into deep relaxation and many activities in this book are designed to help you to do this. Mindfulness meditation* is a relaxation approach which gently focuses the mind on moment-by-moment experience, for example, on the *breath* entering and leaving the nostrils, or on each *part of the body* in turn, or on *sounds* as they occur in our surroundings. Training our attention to focus in this way, without trying to change anything, brings us fully into the present, away from worries about the past or unhelpful imaginings about the future. It is at the heart of Mindfulness-based stress reduction (MBSR)*, an internationally accepted therapeutic approach developed by Jon Kabat-Zinn (2) at the University of Massachusetts Medical Center in the USA, and which has clinically proven benefits for people with depression, anxiety disorders and chronic pain (3).

CHARACTERISTICS OF THE RELAXATION RESPONSE

Breathing slows and deepens

Heart beat slows

Metabolism slows and normalises

Muscles relax

Hormonal activity balances

Blood flow increases to hands and feet

Mindfulness meditations

Choosing where and how we pay attention is the first step to training the mind to be more present and less 'scattered'. Try any of the mindfulness activities below, beginning with five minutes and slowly building up the time you spend in these ways. You will probably notice that the mind tends to skip about all over the place, from thought to thought and away from the present into the past and future. In fact, the mind seems to have a mind of its own! Each time you realise your mind has gone off track, bring it gently back to your mindful activity.

Mindful breathing

Get in touch with your breath by sitting or lying and placing one hand over your belly, or navel area. Notice how the belly rises with the in-breath and drops back with the out-breath. Focus on these physical sensations, with, and then without, the hand in place. There is no need to control or change the breath in any way, just allow it to come and go. Rest in the awareness of the physical sensations of the breath moving in and out of the body.

This is also available as a free audio download on **www.stepbeachpress.co.uk**

Mindful walking

This can be done indoors or outdoors. Focus on a 'pathway' of about 10 steps ahead. Stand with your feet parallel, your knees relaxed, arms held loosely by your sides and your gaze focused softly ahead. Feel the soles of your feet making contact with the ground, then bring your attention to the first step. Slow it right down, so that you are aware of every tiny movement, as the heel rises, the calf muscles engage and the foot gradually leaves the ground and is placed down ahead. Be aware of how the balance in the body shifts, and how the back foot starts to lift from the heel to make the next step. When you complete your 10 mindful steps, turn around, and take 10 mindful steps back to your starting point.

Mindful listening

Sit comfortably and bring your attention to the ears. Be aware of any sounds as they arise and wherever they arise, without searching for them. Allow awareness to open to sounds which are near and far away, in front, behind and inside you, obvious sounds and more subtle sounds, the spaces of silence between sounds.

Mindful body scan

Make yourself comfortable and take your attention to your left foot. Invite your focus onto the sensations in your toes. If your attention wanders, as soon as you notice it has, bring it gently back. Gradually focus on each part of the foot in turn, then the lower leg and upper leg, before taking your attention to your right foot and repeating the procedure. You may need to bring your focus back many, many times or if you are very tired, you may even fall asleep. It doesn't matter. The important point is to accept things as they are. Move your focus onto each part of the body, moving slowly upwards, then down each arm into the hands and fingers, followed by the neck, face and head.

4 Practise the art of visualisation

Practise visualisation to enhance and improve well-being and to achieve your goals.

Throughout this book, you will find ideas and suggestions based on the practice of visualisation. One of the most powerful mental resources we have as humans is our imagination. We can use it to good effect, as when we imagine positive, fulfilling outcomes, or to bad effect, for example, when we imagine all kinds of future catastrophes and fuel our anxiety.

Positive visualisation is a wonderful tool which utilises our imaginations to effect all kinds of changes in how we feel. We can use it to work towards a goal by visualising the process for achieving success, for example, imagining going to the gym and exercising to get fit, or imagining the immune system seeking and destroying cancer cells. We can also use it to create mental pictures of the goal or result

as if it had already occurred, for example, imagining what it is like to be that new, strong, healthy person full of energy and stamina.

The art of visualisation is to use all your senses, not just 'seeing', but hearing, smelling, tasting, and feeling textures, movement and sensations. We all have a dominant sense, but it is helpful to practise using others until your visualisation becomes a richer and richer experience. Visualisation focuses the attention inwards, creating a deeply relaxing, trance state. Trance is a natural state which we all dip into when we daydream, meditate, jog or otherwise become absorbed in our inner thoughts and experiences. It is sometimes called the REM (rapid eye movement) or 'programming state' (which also occurs when we dream at night). When we access REM, we create powerful images and we are open to new learning. Using this language of the unconscious mind to make requests for change and to rehearse those changes through guided imagery (visualisation), is a foundation of hypnotherapy*.

A staircase to relaxation

As a first step, we can use visualisation to create a healthy state of deep relaxation...

Make yourself comfortable in a place where you will not be disturbed. Notice how the body is supported – behind the head and back, under the legs and feet. As you breathe in and out, spend a few moments focusing on the belly rising and falling as the breath enters and leaves, without changing or forcing the breath in any way.

Now imagine that you are standing at the top of a flight of ten steps leading down to a special place of relaxation. This could be a place you remember being in and feeling really calm and peaceful, perhaps a holiday beach, country scene or cosy room, or it could be somewhere you imagine would be the most relaxing place you could possibly be in.

As your breathing begins to slow down, on each outbreath imagine taking one step down your staircase, holding on to a rail if you feel you need to. As you slowly descend, count down from 10 to 1 on each out-breath, looking forward to the scene that awaits you at the bottom. With the final step, imagine walking into your relaxing space.

Use all your senses to create as vivid a place as possible. See the colours, shapes and quality of light. Hear any sounds that add to your sense of relaxation. There may be smells or even tastes that remind you of calm. You may be able to sense textures, for example, the feeling of soft sand beneath your feet, or the warm, silky water of a bath lapping around your body.

Find somewhere to rest in this scene, as you continue to build and enjoy its features. Begin to notice relaxation spreading throughout your body, perhaps starting with your feet and working upwards to your head. Notice how your mind has quietened.

Try this

When you are ready, you can imagine leaving your scene, knowing you can return whenever you wish. Count back from 1 up to 10 as you imagine drifting up the staircase, step by step, and walking back into the room. Open your eyes and take a gentle stretch.

This is also available as a free audio download at **www.stepbeachpress.co.uk**

SEE ALSO
- **WAY 5: What you focus on is what you get** (page 30)
- **WAY 21: Think well, be well** (page 72)

WAY 5

What you focus on is what you get

Understand the power of the Law of Attraction in your life.

'The Law of Attraction' was first described in 1906 by William Walker Atkinson, a very influential figure in the early days of the New Thought Movement (4). Scientists and psychologists who are interested in why certain people succeed in life while others do not, have written prolifically about this psychological phenomenon.

It certainly seems that people who are generally successful in life (ie. they achieve what they set out to achieve) often spend time and energy really focusing on what it is they want. They have a clear vision of how they would like things to be, and once the outcome is achieved, what that will look like, including the ways in which it will differ from the present. This means they know when they have done what they have set out to do, and when it is time to move on to the next step.

The reason business coaches often advise owners of fledgling businesses to write a business plan, is underpinned by the Law of Attraction. Once a budding entrepreneur has developed a clear vision of how they want their business to grow and develop,

they have attuned their consciousness to noticing opportunities, products, people and other resources that will support that vision. It is the same process as when you are weighing up whether to buy a new red hatchback, and suddenly notice red hatchbacks everywhere on the road! They were always there, of course, but now you have 'tuned in' your consciousness to notice them. This can also be explained by understanding how the brain works in terms of noticing or not noticing. The structure of the brain, the gatekeeper to awareness, is the reticular formation. It scans input from the environment, looking out for what is important for survival, or relevant to us. Being clear about our vision and goals harnesses and guides the reticular activation process, just as the Law of Attraction suggests.

The Law of Attraction can, of course, be used to our great detriment if we focus our attention on things we *do not* want. If we are feeling overwhelmed and sad, we can allow our emotional brain to take over and start imagining everything going wrong! For instance, when a long-term relationship breaks up and we are feeling bereft, we might think, 'I will never meet anyone new, I am so boring and unattractive...'. If we continue to focus on those feelings, we do become boring by going on about everything that's wrong and that in itself is pretty unattractive! It's no wonder that people will start avoiding us.

SEE ALSO
- **WAY 4: Practise the art of visualisation** (page 28)
- **WAY 21: Think well, be well** (page 72)

Create a vision of what you want

Try this exercise when you know you need to significantly refocus your attention.

Set aside some quiet time where you won't be interrupted. Use one of the relaxation techniques described in **WAY 3: Take a mindful approach to relaxation**, page 26). Once you feel calm and relaxed, gently bring your focus to the future, as if you were looking at a cinema screen. How do you want it to look, what do you want it to sound and feel like? Put in place the important parts of this vision – the place, the people, how people (including yourself) are acting, what they are saying, how they are saying it. Make it as vivid as you can, adding detail as it comes to mind. Get a sense of how good it feels to have achieved your vision.

From this place in the future, ask yourself, 'What was the first step I took to achieve my vision? What was the next step, and the next?' Imagine how you have moved, step by step, towards where you are now.

When you are ready, bring yourself back to full consciousness. Draw pictures, make notes or record what you have experienced. Use this to formulate your vision in more detail and put it up where you can see it every day. You might wish to add to it, cutting out pictures or words which seem to resonate from magazines. You can do this exercise over and over again, adding more detail and embedding your vision more deeply in your mind.

Try this

Tip: Your imagination is your 'reality generator' so learn to use it wisely! Make sure your attention is focused on what you want more of in your life. Throughout this book, there are plenty of exercises that show you how to harness the power of your imagination in order to achieve changes. When you decide to make a change in your life, however big or small, a key rule is to make sure you spend some time visualising what that will be like, following the guidelines in **WAY 4: Practise the art of visualisation, page 28.**

For example, if you want to give up smoking, visualise yourself glowing with health, smelling fresh and clean, wearing beautiful clothes that you could choose with all the money you will have saved. Then any time you are tempted to fall back into the habit, you can bring this image to mind and ideally accompany it with a statement to yourself which further imbeds the change you are making such as, 'I am saying no to cigarettes because my health and happiness are now my focus.'

6

Connect with your resources

Tap into your internal (often hidden) resources and also utilise what's around you.

Whenever we feel overwhelmed with emotion, we can lose sight of all the good things in our lives. This includes the good things *within* us (our skills, talents, experiences etc) and also *around us* (our friends, family, community and other support systems which help us access what we need). Psychologists often refer to these as 'internal and external resources'. It often seems that at the very time we most need these resources, we are most likely to forget about them. This is because when we feel stressed or overwhelmed our thinking

brain shuts down (see **WAY 2: Switch off the stress response**, page 22 and **WAY 17: Don't flip your lid! Stay cool and calm**, page 62) and then we can easily feel 'all at sea' without a crew or oars! Given the way our brains function, it can be much more helpful to tune into our resources when we feel relatively relaxed and able to recognise them. If we leave it until we slip into the grip of negative thinking and emotions, we may end up believing thoughts such as, 'I have no real friends', or 'Nothing I have ever done has been successful'. Then we *really* feel un-resourced and this can fuel the negative cycle of depressive thinking which we cover in detail in Chapter 3.

SEE ALSO
- ***Chapter 6: Set Goals and Boost Your Motivation*** (page 85)

Tip: If you find that either your internal or external resources seem to be lacking, first check this out with someone you trust. Is this reality, or is it that you are just feeling a bit stuck or low at the moment and have trouble identifying them? After this, if it still seems that internal or external resources are on the low side, turn to Chapter 6 on goal setting which will help you to set some realistic goals around and take steps towards building more resources.

This is a whole life's work; resources come and go. Having a list gives you something to remind yourself of what you can draw on, particularly during difficult times. You may wish to review them from time to time, particularly when things change in your life. These resources are like your emotional bank account, they will keep you afloat on a rainy day when you're feeling down, so keep checking in with the balance!

Recognise and use what is good

Begin by using a relaxation or breathing technique from **WAY 2: Switch off the stress response** or **WAY 3: Take a mindful approach to relaxation.** This will give you the best possible chance of tuning into your resources, as your thinking brain will be clear and fully alert.

Then write down your internal resources. You could start with the things you are most proud of in your life. Include in this list things you have done/achieved eg. challenges you have risen to, qualifications, career developments, commitments to family/friends, skills you have acquired in any area of your life, qualities of yours that friends have complimented you on, and so on. All of this can be hard to think about because it is not something we tend to focus on, and so we can often draw a blank when trying to do so. Try this tip: if someone asked a close friend/family member what is good about you, what would they say?

Next, write down your external resources: Who in your life can you trust, have a laugh with, or rely on in a crisis? What hobbies and interests do you have? What clubs or groups do you belong to? What are you thankful for at work? What community resources are helpful/useful for you eg. library, community centre, cinema, parks? Where can you find information when you need it? What financial means do you have if a crisis hits?

Try this

1 2 3 4 5 6 **7 8**
9 10 11 12 13 14
15 16 17 18 19
20 21 22 23 24
25 26 27 28 29
30 31 32 33 34
35 36 37 38 39
40 41 42 43 44
45 46 47 48 49

Chapter 2

DEAL WITH STRESS, ANXIETY, PANIC AND WORRY

The stress response can be triggered by our fears, anxiety and worry and can sometimes lead us into a full-blown panic attack. This chapter will help you to avoid unnecessary stress in your life by concentrating on what you *can* change. You will learn how to evoke a sense of calm in stressful situations, and how to handle or avoid panic attacks to help you stay in control of your life. You can practise techniques for reducing the amount of time spent worrying and some emergency strategies for distracting yourself away from fear, anxiety and worry. Reducing your response to stress in these ways will enhance your well-being and put you back in control of your life.

WAY 7
Concentrate on what you CAN change

Learn to let go of what you can't change and free up spare energy.

How often to you catch yourself saying things like...

'If only dad would be kinder/ listen to me/ have more time for the kids!'

'Why does she behave like that? It's wrong, why doesn't she realise it?'

'People are so racist; they have to realise that they are hurting people. It's terrible!'

'The Government doesn't care about the little people, we can't change anything!'

'My boss never listens to me, there's no point in even trying to talk to him!'

...and how does it make you feel when you say something like this, either to yourself or others? Angry? Frustrated? Powerless? Allowing yourself to focus on what other people are doing wrong and how it should be different is a dead-end path that only leads to misery – for you! The people responsible for the behaviour itself are getting off scot free while you moan and ruminate about what they are doing!

SEE ALSO
• *Chapter 6: Set Goals and Boost Your Motivation* (page 85)

Direct your energy to where it can be transformational

Make a list of the things you know cause you most stress or worry and divide the list into three parts:

1. What stresses you about the world in general (eg. global warming, child slavery, bad weather etc)?
2. What stresses you most about other people (eg. road rage, others not listening, lying to you etc)?
3. What stresses you the most from inside yourself (eg. taking on too much, feeling nervous in crowds, difficulty trusting others etc)?

Now, look at the list and decide for each one, what you can do about each point and what you have to let go of. Remember that you cannot change other people! Trying to make people behave differently is a recipe for disappointment. By letting go of your attempts to change others, you free up that wasted energy to concentrate on what you can influence.

Interestingly, one of the most effective ways of helping others to change is to change the way you behave. If you let go of trying to change someone else, they will pick up on that shift. They may notice that

you no longer make negative comments, or even that you have stopped unconsciously sighing when they do something you don't like! However, remember that it is still possible this won't shift their behaviour if they are not ready to change (see **'Cycle of change'** on page 122 for more information).

Either way, giving another person time and non-judgmental space to change is far more effective than nagging, which can have the opposite effect. Of course, you also have the power to remove yourself from people behaving in ways you don't like or to limit contact with people who are making you unhappy. You could consider using these strategies to address items on your list referring to other people.

When you have made the list of what you can do for things that stress you, pick the one that is most important to you now and decide when you will take the first step of doing something differently. By realising what you cannot change (and it's only you that suffers if you try) you really do free up the energy to make some positive changes in your life.

Try this

Tip: You might also like to consider focusing this activity on different areas of your life (eg. relationships, work, leisure, domestic matters). Work out what stresses you in each area, then hone in on what you can actually change and what you have to accept or let go of.

WAY 8

Create an anchor for calm

Learn to instantly evoke a sense of complete calm, even in stressful situations.

Anxiety is made up of physical sensations, emotions and thoughts, all of which we can learn to master and calm. Cultivating a sense of calm means that we are functioning in an optimal way. We are physically relaxed, able to step back from our own and others' emotions and can make the best decisions about how we want to respond.

Resource anchoring is a powerful technique from the world of neuro-linguistic programming (or NLP). We can learn to set up an 'anchor' which triggers a state of calm. An anchor is a sensory trigger which becomes associated with a particular response or state. On a simple level, the sight of a red traffic light prompts us to stop. However, we respond unconsciously to anchors all the time, to both good and bad effect, for example, when the warmth of a sunny morning prompts us to feel good, or the smell of a hospital makes us feel nervous or even sick! The association is strengthened by repetition and by the level of emotion that accompanies it. We can learn how to create our own anchor to elicit the desired state of calm in difficult situations, using the guidelines opposite.

SEE ALSO
• **WAY 4: Practise the art of visualisation**
  (page 28)

> Tip: Think of a calm person you know. What is it about them that communicates a sense of calm? How do they look? How do they move? What do they say? What is their tone of voice?

Get anchored

1. Elicit a state of calm
In order to elicit any state you need to develop a vivid sense of what 'calm' feels like. You can do this in two ways:

- When you are relaxed, think of a time when you felt really calm. Where were you? What was it about the scene that felt calming – the sights, sounds, textures, smells? What did being calm really feel like?
- Act as though you are calm. Move around and change your body posture and breathing until you get a sense that this is 'being calm'. Even if you don't feel calm, changing your physiology in this way will send powerful signals to the unconscious mind to move towards a state of calm.

2. Create your anchor
An anchor can be...
- *visual,* such as a hand gesture
- *auditory*, such as a word or tone of voice
- *kinaesthetic*, such as a touch.

It should be unique, ie. not used for any other reason, and easy to repeat exactly. It also needs to be discreet, so that no one else is aware that you are using it. An example might be gently squeezing a thumb against a particular finger on one hand, or silently intoning a particular word or phrase.

3. Use your anchor
Practise eliciting a state of calm using the ideas above. Just before you feel you have reached a peak of calm, apply your anchor for a count of 3 (if you wait until you have peaked, you may anchor to a declining sense of calm). Practise this again and again in a relaxed state, at least 20 times, so that it becomes dependable.

4. Future pace

Finally, imagine a stressful situation in which you might wish to use your calm anchor. See and feel yourself using your anchor, staying calm and acting resourcefully. Notice something in the situation which can remind you to use the anchor in future, for example, the sight of a particular person, standing up to speak, walking through the dentist's door.

This is also available as a free audio download at **www.stepbeachpress.co.uk**

WAY 9

Don't panic!

Recognising the signs of a panic attack and taking action to regain a sense of control is something we can all learn to do.

A panic attack is the same as the body's normal fear reaction, but it is happening inappropriately, that is, in an ordinary situation. As we saw in **WAY 2: Switch off the stress response**, our essential survival mechanism, the stress response, can be set off at times when we don't need it to. The stress response can catch us unawares and tip us into an experience of panic.

This can happen for several reasons. The limbic system* may have learned to associate features of our surroundings with danger, because they were present at a time when we experienced a high degree of fear or trauma in the past. These features in themselves might be entirely non-threatening, for example, a harmless spider, a crowded or confined space, or the smell of a hospital ward. However, they have become associated with the feeling of being in danger, and this 'pattern matching' is at the heart of both panic attacks and phobias.

Panic attacks can also arise from the misuse of our powerful imaginations. Just imagining all kinds of disaster scenarios, for example, when we misinterpret bodily symptoms and convince ourselves that we have an incurable illness, can escalate our levels of fear until we trigger off the stress response – even though there is nothing dangerous in the present. Thirdly, our level of stress might be so high that a further challenge pushes our anxiety over the edge – the straw that breaks the camel's back.

Other factors that may prompt a panic attack include:

- toxins or chemicals in our system, for example, caffeine or some drugs
- negative thinking and worrying
- anger, rage and other intense emotions
- accident and injury
- piling pressure on ourselves (a good example being the 'adrenaline* junkie').

The physical symptoms which mobilise our bodies to get out of danger (see **The Stress Response in Action diagram**, page 22) can be frightening to experience at times when there is nothing to run away from and no one to fight. Escalating blood pressure, pounding heart and quick, shallow breathing may be accompanied by shaking in the limbs and tingling or numbness in the arms and hands, as blood flow and oxygen go to the major muscles. We may feel sick, experience chest pain or even feel we are choking. Panic attacks are often accompanied by extreme thoughts:

> I'm going to die!
> I'm having a heart attack!
> I'm going crazy!
> I can't breathe!
> This isn't real!

We can take the power out of these thoughts by countering them with helpful thoughts such as, '*I've been in this situation before*', '*If I breathe slowly, I know it will pass.*'

Tip: Hold your breath for up to 15 seconds to avoid hyperventilation, before resuming calm, slower breathing or **7/11 breathing** (see page 24). Remember that panic attacks cannot harm you and usually last for no longer than 10 minutes, even if allowed to follow their normal course. However, it is important to seek professional advice if you are experiencing repeated attacks.

Panic attacks (and high levels of stress) arise from a spiralling cycle of physical symptoms, thoughts, emotions and actions. These can be avoided by learning new skills: reducing physical symptoms by learning relaxation and controlled breathing (see **WAY 2: Switch off the stress response**, page 22 and **WAY 3: Take a mindful approach to relaxation**, page 26); reducing emotional and mental symptoms by tackling worry, negative thinking and

anger (see Chapters 3 and 4); and changing behaviour so that you can act resourcefully in challenging situations. Staying in a difficult situation by using the technique below, 'tells' the amygdala*, the alarm system in your brain, that you are safe and that there is no need to fight or run away. This can give you a vital sense of getting back in control and can weaken unhelpful associations between the situation and the alarm trigger.

The AWARE technique

Try going through the steps below when you feel your anxiety levels rising. Repeated practice can boost your confidence, break the associations of the past and re-set your 'burglar alarm' to normal levels.

A – Accept the anxiety and try to go with the experience. Fighting anxiety just fuels the flames.

W – Watch or observe the anxiety curiously, without judging it as good or bad. You can scale its intensity from 1 to 10 to get your rational brain back into gear. Remember that you are much more than your anxiety.

A – Act normal by continuing to do what you were intending to do. Use 7/11 breathing to regulate the breath.

R – Repeat the steps. Continue accepting the anxiety, watching it and acting normal until it goes down to a comfortable level.

E – Expect the best. What you fear may never happen. You will surprise yourself by how effectively you can handle the situation. As a longer term strategy, you may want to make changes to your lifestyle, by ensuring that you are meeting your emotional needs (see **WAY 1: Bulletproof your happiness**, page 20), reducing sources of stress (see **Way 7: Concentrate on what you CAN change**, page 36), setting goals (*Chapter 6*) and breaking unhelpful habits (*Chapter 9*).

Try this

WAY 10

Put worry in its place

Reducing the time spent worrying can lower your stress levels and improve your health.

Worrying involves a constant repetition of thoughts which lead nowhere. Whereas thinking leads to action and hopefully, relief, worrying about real or imaginary problems triggers the stress response and raises the levels of stress hormones in our bodies (see **WAY 2: Switch off the stress response**, page 22). Continual worrying about something which cannot be re-solved can lead to rumination which is a major feature of depression (see **WAY 16: Avoid the depression cycle**, page 56).

Worrying can take two forms: 'real worries' based on real life situations, and 'unfounded worries' based on the imagination. Each can be dealt with in slightly different ways.

Worrying about real-life issues needs to be kept in its place as a first step to tackling any problems in a resourceful way. A cognitive behaviour therapy (CBT)* approach is to allocate 'worry time' which is clearly ring-fenced, for example, 20 minutes at a particular time of day. Having a set place to worry or even a 'worry chair' can help to delineate this time even more. For the rest of the day, we can try to detract away from the first signs of worrying, knowing that our worry time will come! During worry time, we should do nothing except worry. In practice, although this can be quite challenging, it can sometimes help to put worry into perspective.

Unfounded worries can be based on anxiety-fuelling beliefs, for example, imagined illnesses, or superstition. Our powerful imaginations can take us into all kinds of future disasters. Through deep relaxation, we can learn to think about the worry while feeling relaxed and without emotion.

Dealing with unfounded worries might require specialist help, for example, from a CBT therapist or hypnotherapist.

SEE ALSO
- **WAY 11: SOS strategies** (page 44)
- **WAY 12: Tune in and tune out of negative thinking** (page 48)
- **WAY 13: Stand up to the bully of negative thinking** (page 50)

> Tip: Learn to realistically evaluate future 'threats'. Rate from 1 to 10 how likely it is to happen. What is the very worst that could happen? What is the best that could happen? The likelihood is that the reality will fall somewhere in between.

Worry time

Rather than comfortably worrying in a warm bed or on a soft settee, find an upright chair for your worry time, and allocate a specific half hour of the day (but not right before bedtime). Choose a place you will not be disturbed.

During this time, consciously seek out worrying thoughts about everything you are concerned about and worry intensely. You may just worry aimlessly for the whole time, or use some time to work out any steps to deal with your concerns. Once the time is up, stop worrying and go and do something you enjoy and which absorbs your attention. If you haven't finished worrying, allocate the rest to the next worry time.

Setting aside time like this can help you to block out intrusive thoughts, as you know you will be giving them attention later. In between worry times, postpone worrying by clapping your hands and saying to yourself something like, 'Stop! Not now! Later!', preferably out loud, and then distract yourself into doing something else. You might like to note down a worry to focus on later.

If you start to worry at night, keep a notebook alongside your bed and jot down your worries for your worry time. Imagine locking them up in a black box under the bed, until this time comes around.

More activities based on worry time can be found in Ad Kerkhof's book '*Stop Worrying*' (5).

Try this

Further tips about managing worrying:

- Understand your worry patterns. How do they start, what comes next, how do they end? Recognising the pattern gives you an opportunity to regain control and change it.
- Check whether you are meeting your basic emotional needs (see **WAY 1: Bulletproof your happiness**, page 20), and are getting enough sleep (see **WAY 25: Clean up your sleep act**, page 80)
- Laughter is a natural medicine for dissolving worry and anxiety, without side effects! Watch funny films, ask friends to email good jokes or funny stories, and spend time with people who like to laugh.

- Learn to relax deeply, which helps you to take a step back from worries, come up with solutions and see the bigger picture (see **WAY 4: Practise the art of visualisation**, page 28, and **WAY 8: Create an anchor for calm**, page 38).
- Use mindfulness* practice to turn off busy and worrisome thoughts (see **WAY 3: Take a mindful approach to relaxation**, page 26).

Approaches which combat negative thinking will also help to reduce worrying (see *Chapter 3: Control Negative Thinking and Avoid Depression*, page 47).

WAY 11

SOS strategies

When you start to feel fearful or over emotional, it's essential to have a few tricks up your sleeve to get you quickly back in control.

Many of us who tend to get anxious or worry find it difficult to stop, once our stress response is activated.

Practising relaxation or 7/11 breathing (see **WAY 2: Switch off the stress response**, p22) can help us to notice what we are thinking and then to 'stand back' and observe our thoughts and worries. We can then make a judgment about how useful (or not) they are.

Once we notice that we are engaging in unproductive worrying or imaginings, we can then distract ourselves and break the pattern. Different distracting activities work better for different people, but these could include:

• Get in touch with other people, for example, by phoning a friend
• Walk briskly around the block or the garden
• Spend a couple of minutes using 7/11 breathing (see **WAY 2: Switch off the stress response**, page 22)
• Write down the thoughts you're having and test out the evidence for them (see **WAY 13: Stand up to the bully of negative thinking**, page 50)

• Listen to a relaxation recording
• Do some housework
• Do some vigorous exercise, eg. star jumps, running up and down stairs
• Count backwards from 300 in 3s (this engages the rational, thinking part of the brain)
• Mow the lawn, bake a cake or do something else you can enjoy and get absorbed in

Even practising one of the above for as little as 30 seconds can help to break the chain of thoughts and physiological responses which can spiral into panic or a bout of worrying.

SEE ALSO
• ***Chapter 3: Control Negative Thinking and Avoid Depression*** (page 47)

Tip: SOS

Remember this acronym to help distract away from worry and anxiety:

S – 'Stop!'
O – 'Observe'
S – 'Steer away'.

My distraction activities

Write a list of distraction activities you might use to divert away from the early sensations or thoughts associated with fear, anxiety and worry. Use the list opposite as a source of ideas.

You may wish to pin them up in a place you can readily see them, should the need arise. Longer term, you can work towards doing without these SOS strategies by:

ensuring that you are meeting your emotional needs (**WAY 1: Bulletproof your happiness**, page 20), practising regular relaxation (**WAY 3: Take a mindful approach to relaxation**, page 26), or transforming any negative thoughts (**WAY 12: Tune in and tune out of negative thinking**, page 48, and **WAY 13: Stand up to the bully of negative thinking**, page 50).

Try this

1 2 3 4 5 6 7 8
9 10 11 **12 13 14**
15 16 17 18 19
20 21 22 23 24
25 26 27 28 29
30 31 32 33 34
35 36 37 38 39
40 41 42 43 44
45 46 47 48 49

Chapter 3

CONTROL NEGATIVE THINKING AND AVOID DEPRESSION

How we think is closely linked to how we feel and how we then act in our lives. We can sometimes believe that we *are* our thoughts and this can lead us into a state of hopelessness and helplessness. Negative thinking can trigger the stress response and is at the heart of depression. This chapter will help you to separate yourself from your thoughts, so that you can be objective about their content. You can learn about common errors of thinking so that you can guard against them. It is important to challenge negative thoughts and consciously change them, and there are several techniques included for doing just this. Finally, we cover the importance of understanding the cycle of depression which can be triggered by constant, negative thinking, called rumination. Learning to avoid this pattern of thinking will help to ensure that you continue experiencing motivation and pleasure in life.

WAY 12

Tune in and tune out of negative thinking

Realise how negative thinking can keep you stuck.

Throughout this book, we will share with you a few of the basic CBT* skills so that you can benefit from this therapeutic approach. Negative thinking can be toxic. This is because negative thoughts can be highly emotionally arousing, triggering the stress response to perceived danger, or producing euphoria. Both of these states disable our 'thinking brain' and lead us into problematic behaviour. Here, we provide you with the first step to taking control of negative thinking.

The observing self

The first and most fundamental skill is to start to become *aware* of your thoughts. This sounds simple, but we are so conditioned to accept our thoughts as fact that we identify with them to the point that we feel we *are* our thoughts.

SEE ALSO

• **WAY 14: Mind your language** (page 52)
• **WAY 15: Beat the blues** (page 54)

By becoming aware of our thoughts, we give ourselves a very powerful tool: we separate ourselves from our thoughts, so that we can be objective about their accuracy.

This has been called stepping into our observing self*, a term introduced by psychiatrist Arthur Deikman (6), to explain the part of our mind that 'steps back' from the world of thought and sees what is going on inside it from a more detached perspective, rather than being blindly led by our thoughts as if they were fact.

When you learn to do this and keep doing this, it can be surprisingly freeing. You are no longer a slave to negative thoughts that can, otherwise, pull you down and stop you moving on in your life. You can realise that thoughts are just that – thoughts – and that you have a *choice* to not be a slave to negative thoughts (see **'Stay in the present'**, page 59, for a way of utilising the observing self in this way).

Tip: Use the chart in **WAY 13: Stand up to the bully of negative thinking**, page 50, to replace any thinking errors with more constructive thoughts based on reality and not let them run your life anymore!

Discover the dirty tricks of negative thoughts!

Try this

It takes courage to admit to ourselves that we have been slaves to negative thinking, but once we realise that these thoughts are *not* fact, our lives can turn around! Below is the master list of thinking 'errors' that trip us all up at times.

Take a look at the list below and see if you can identify with any of these styles of negative thinking, then *be on your guard* for when they occur. You might like to name the part of you that can get caught up in these patterns of thinking, so that you can quickly identify when 'he' or 'she' tries to creep in and ruin your day! For instance, if you are prone to making a mountain out of a mole hill, or 'catastrophising', you might say to yourself, 'Uh oh, here comes Catastrophising Cathy, I had better cross the street away from her so that I can stay in my rational mind!'

COMMON FAULTY WAYS OF THINKING

Black-and-white thinking
(It *must* be one thing or another)
Only seeing a 'right' way and a 'wrong' way, without allowing any possibilities in between, eg. unless everything is right, then it's all a total failure! (see **WAY 15: Beat the blues**, page 54)

Catastrophising
Jumping to the worst possible conclusion in any given situation, without considering all the other possibilities, eg. you sneeze once and know you are coming down with flu again.

Over-generalising
Because something has happened once, believing that will always be the case, eg. you went to a busy restaurant and felt panicky and now you believe that you will always feel this way when you go out to eat.

Focusing on the negative
When you ignore the positives in any situation, eg, you feel devastated and a 'failure' that you have lost your job, while ignoring all the ways you have succeeded in life – you have lost jobs before and always found another (often better) one; you have good networks; you are skilled and other areas of your life are working well.

Jumping to unfounded conclusions
Allowing your imagination to take over and believe the fantasies it comes up with, eg. a friend makes an off-the-cuff remark without thinking, which you take personally and then jump to the conclusion that they no longer like you or want your friendship.

Believing and using controlling statements
Using words such as 'should' 'must', ought', 'never', and 'always' means that we are being controlled by 'rules' that we have made up for ourselves somewhere along the line, or that someone else has made them up for us! Let them be warning signs that someone else is doing our thinking for us! They are usually reflections of someone else's views that we have unconsciously taken on and which can keep us trapped in fixed and unhelpful ways of living.

13

Stand up to the bully of negative thinking

Learn how to challenge negative thoughts and come back to reality.

In **WAY 12: Tune in and tune out of negative thinking**, page 48, we focused on the fact that thoughts are just thoughts, rather than unmovable facts that must be accepted. Thoughts are reflections of your mood, and that mood will affect the perspective you have on what is currently going on in your life and around you.

We all have the power to start noticing our thoughts and consciously changing them for the better, so that we have a more balanced and objective perspective. Constructive thoughts are far more helpful to us and will improve our mood.

This is not to say that it is easy to change our thoughts; it takes practice and perseverance, but it *is* possible to harness the power of realistic, helpful thinking, rather than allowing negative thoughts to drag us down and prevent us from achieving our goals. Once you begin to see the results of letting go of negative thinking, you really start to experience how liberating this can be.

Tip: If you are feeling low, thinking more objectively and trying to find evidence against a negative thought can seem difficult. This is because in an emotional state, your brain sometimes discounts the more objective evidence and you can get 'locked' into negative thinking. In order to help your brain work more constructively, use 7/11 breathing for a few minutes (see **WAY 2: Switch off the stress response**, page 22). You might also imagine that you are advising your best friend (rather than yourself) to look for evidence. What would you say to them if they were thinking these thoughts? Looking at your situation from a different viewpoint can help you be more objective and see all the available evidence to counter negative thoughts.

Creating balanced thoughts

Use this chart to map out thoughts you have identified which are negative, unhelpful or unbalanced. We have used the example of a situation where a friend walks past you in the street without acknowledging you and the negative thoughts this can spiral into.

Situation	Negative thought	Evidence for this thought	Evidence against this thought	More balanced thought/ alternative explanation
A friend ignored me when I walked past her in the street.	She saw me and ignored me on purpose, she has never liked me.	She didn't speak to me at that Christmas party. She rarely smiles at me.	She has talked to me at other gatherings. Maybe she had other stuff on her mind or wasn't feeling like talking to anybody.	She might not have seen me or was distracted. I will call her later and check she's OK.
Try this	If people ignore me, I must be unlikeable or boring.	A previous boyfriend told me I was boring. I often end up on my own at parties.	I'm not always alone at parties, I met some nice people at the last two I went to and had a good time. Friends do call me and ask me to do things.	Maybe sometimes I do feel boring, but not all the time. I do have some good friends. I can't be liked by everybody, that's impossible.

Here is the process broken down:

Step 1 Write down the situation that occurred that led you to feel unhappy.

Step 2 Write down the thoughts that occurred as a result of that event and then any other thoughts that led on from that.

Step 3 Write down what you believe to be any evidence to support each thought.

Step 4 Write down any evidence that you think counteracts this thought.

Step 5 Now, considering evidence for and against, write down a more balanced and realistic thought, which accounts for all evidence.

Getting everything down in writing helps to bypass an emotional brain, which is flooded with stress hormones and is disabling you from seeing the situation objectively. Then stopping to think about evidence against each negative thought gets you to start seeing the bigger picture, thereby stepping out of narrow black-and-white thinking.

WAY 14

Mind your language

Discover the power your self-talk has over your mood.

There are certain patterns of thinking that get reflected in what we say to others, and also to ourselves in the form of 'self-talk', which block us from living optimistically and with joy. Controlling language limits us to 'fixed rules' for living and stops us from seeing all the possibilities in life.

These patterns of thinking and speech nearly always come from our early conditioning, ie. what we were taught as young children about how the world operates, who we are in it and what is 'OK' and 'not OK'. Of course as children, we accept these assumptions as the absolute truth. However, when we become adults, we may want to start to question some of these assumptions, particularly if they are not helpful to our growth and happiness.

There are three words that many of us use frequently and without question in our day-to-day speech and thoughts, which do *not* serve us well. These three words tell us that there is only one way to look at life, that things are either right or wrong, and that there are no other possibilities. Of course, there may be rare occasions where that might be true, but generally speaking, it is far more accurate to say that there are many ways of looking at one situation, there are numerous possibilities in life, things are constantly changing, and that it's likely that people will have different opinions.

So, what are these three *toxic* little words? They are: **SHOULD, OUGHT** and **MUST**!

All three of these words impose fixed rules, they tell us there are no other possibilities, this is how it is and nothing can change. Using them may limit both ourselves and other people we put on the receiving end.

Here are some examples of how they are frequently used:

'I **MUST** always look perfect'
'I **OUGHT** to be better at this'
'I **SHOULD** be half a stone lighter'
'I **SHOULD** have passed that test'
'I **MUST** be so stupid'
'I **STILL** haven't found a loving partner'
'I **MUST** be unlovable'
'I **OUGHT** to get a more interesting job'

Do you see how, by using those words, you close down other perfectly plausible possibilities in any given situation? The person who hasn't found a loving partner might be looking in the wrong places. *Who says* you must look perfect all the time? How boring not to just let go sometimes. *Who says* you must be better at something? You can't be good at everything! So if you want your life to stay stuck, to rob yourself of joy, happiness and curiosity about life, keep using those words!

Don't let your language trap you into fixed rules

The way out of these fixed rules of language is to *question* them. Be on guard and every time you hear yourself say one of these words to yourself or others, and question it. A really simple and useful way to do this is simply to say, '*Who says?*' in response to 'shoulds', 'musts' and 'oughts'. They came from somewhere but they just might not be relevant anymore, so maybe it's time to let go of them...?

Try this

Tip: Imagine that there is an 'alarm' attached to 'shoulds', 'musts' and 'oughts!' Whenever you catch yourself saying any of those words, picture this alarm ringing loudly in your head, warning you to run a mile from that old conditioning. Give yourself a break and live freely in the here and now.

WAY 15

Beat the blues

Increase the flexibility of your thinking to avoid the helplessness trap and get back in control.

Negative thinking patterns are at the heart of depression. People with depression see the world in black-and-white terms. They use absolute words such as 'always' or 'never', 'all' or 'nothing', finding it difficult to see the shades of grey between the two extremes. For example, rather than noticing that they feel 'a little bit better' today, they may continue to say that they 'feel awful' and that 'everything is terrible'. Increasing our flexibility of thinking gives us back a sense of control and the ability to cope with the ever-present change and uncertainties of life.

Scaling is a simple method of breaking down 'all or nothing' thinking that holds problems in place. It engages two powerful aspects of our minds – the thinking brain and the ability we have to observe ourselves – to rate different aspects of how we are feeling. We can rate with numbers, shades of a colour, a musical scale, weather conditions or any other system that fills in the two extremes with a

gentler continuum of options. This moves us out of anxiety or emotion, and into making finer distinctions about our feelings and our progress towards improved well-being.

The American psychologist Martin Seligman and colleagues developed the concept of 'learned helplessness' as a way of understanding depression (7). Arising from observations of animals, they described it as a psychological condition in which a human being or an animal has learned to act or behave helplessly in a particular situation, even when they actually *have* the power to change an unpleasant or even harmful circumstance.

People who are depressed often feel that they have no control over what happens to them because of the way in which they interpret life's events. Their pessimistic style of thinking means that they tend to see 'bad' events as *permanent*, affecting *the whole* of their lives and to do with their own *personal failings*. On the other hand, 'good' events are seen as *temporary, specific* to one part of their lives and to do with *external* circumstances, for example, a 'lucky break'. One way out of these patterns of thinking is to start looking for small things that you *can* control.

SEE ALSO
- **WAY 1: Bulletproof your happiness** (page 20)
- **WAY 28: Set realistic goals** (page 88)

Get back in the driving seat

It is easy to feel that things are 'out of your control', so from time to time, it is useful to check out how much control you do have in your life. Write down some headings which describe different areas of your life, for example, work, family, home environment, holidays, leisure.

Now rate your perceived level of control in each, from 0 – no control, to 10 – maximum control. For those areas where you have scored low, think about some factors you *can* control, however small.

Now get really specific. What will you do this week that will get you one step up that scale?

Noticing and making small, positive changes can help us to avoid the helplessness/hopelessness trap. Here is an example:

Friends (current rating 5/10)

"I notice that some friends make me feel a bit better when I am around them, but others seem to drain my energy, especially when they say negative and unhelpful things."

"This week I am going to plan to see Alec and Bhavna, but will say 'No' to the invitation that includes Molly."

Tip: If you tend to make global statements about how you feel, try this practice. Rate how 'down' or 'low' you feel from 0 – as 'low' as you could possibly feel, to 10 – as good as you could possibly imagine feeling. You could rate at key points in the day, for example, first thing, going to work, before going to bed. As the days go by, notice times when your rating is slightly higher. What are you thinking or doing that is making the difference? Then, do more of these things.

WAY 16 Avoid the depression cycle

Understanding the link between rumination and depression is an important step to maintaining pleasure in life.

Depression is often characterised by a loss of energy, motivation and pleasure in day-to-day life and activities. An important factor behind these symptoms is too much negative rumination. This happens when we churn around the same hopeless thoughts and are unable to resolve their content through any action. The result is over-arousal of the emotional centres in the limbic system, which triggers the stress response (see page 22) and reduces levels of serotonin (the 'feel-good' chemical) in the brain.

Research psychologist Joe Griffin's work at the Human Givens Institute in London (8) suggests that when people ruminate in a negative way, they tend to over-dream at night, since a function of REM sleep could be to discharge arousal 'left over' from the day, so that the higher neocortex can deal with the emotionally arousing situations of the next day. Over-dreaming deprives the sleeper from restful, recuperative deep sleep and this in turn, leads to exhaustion the next morning. No wonder that we feel less inclined to do the things which give us pleasure. We then feel down, ruminate more, dream more and find ourselves feeling even lower, and so the cycle continues.

CYCLE OF DEPRESSION

Negative thinking and rumination

Over-dreaming

Loss of motivation/ doing pleasurable things

Exhaustion in the morning

So how can we avoid getting into this downward cycle of depression? Examining the nature of our rumination can be a starting point...

NEGATIVE THINKING

As we saw in **WAY 15: Beat the blues**, page 54, depression is characterised by a certain style of negative thinking. Use the ideas in this chapter of the book to challenge those thoughts and start creating more hopeful thoughts. Learning to say 'Stop!' when you notice a negative thought, and practising the art of positive thinking is like creating a new, clear pathway in the mind, while allowing the old one to become overgrown and impenetrable.

PAST FOCUS

If rumination is focused on the past and what has gone wrong, it doesn't have to mean that tomorrow will be the same. Changing what you do now will change your future, whereas doing what you always did will mean that you continue to get what you always got! Sometimes we can learn from looking at what we did in the past that worked well for us.

GUILT

Sometimes there is a guilt factor present, for example, feeling that we are 100 per cent to blame for how bad things are, or that we are bad or faulty in some way. If so, we can challenge these thoughts, for example, by asking ourselves what would our partner or best friend say if they heard us making these kinds of statements (see **WAY 13: Stand up to the bully of negative thinking**, page 50). How else could we respond in a situation, other than feeling guilty?

PERFECTIONISM

If perfectionism is a problem, we can ask ourselves whether we are trying to please someone else and give ourselves permission to do things in a less than perfect way.

At the same time as exploring our rumination patterns, we need to take regular, deep relaxation to calm our minds and put things back in perspective. Above all, we need to remember to meet our emotional needs (see **WAY 1: Bulletproof your happiness**, page 20), ensuring that we are giving ourselves the psychological 'nutrition' to feel fulfilled in our lives. We may need to identify the resources we have (see **WAY 6: Connect with your resources**, page 32) and develop our confidence and social skills in order to get 'out and about' again (see Chapter 7). As we start to take up interesting activities again, mental or physical, serotonin levels in the brain increase, which regulate our REM sleep and make us feel further motivated to meet our needs and do the things we enjoy.

NOTE

If you think you are suffering from depression, you need to seek medical help.

Tip: When relaxed, ask yourself how would it be if you were to wake up tomorrow feeling a bit better? What might you be able to do? See yourself in this new scene, looking brighter and being more active. Float into that new you. How does it feel?

Stay in the present

Mindfulness is a powerful practice for both calming the mind and body and for keeping the focus in the present, away from the problems of the past or the imagined catastrophes of the future (see **WAY 3: Take a mindful approach to relaxation**, page 26). It has been shown to help people break out of the downward spiral of mood and prevent the pattern of recurring bouts of depression (9,10).

Use any of the relaxation practices in Chapter 1. Then, when you are ready, bring your awareness to your thoughts. Notice thoughts as they arise, as they linger in the mind, and as they eventually dissolve and disappear. There is no need to try to control these thoughts in any way. It is as if they

are projected onto a film screen and you can just sit, watching the screen, waiting for a thought or image to arise. When it does, attend to it as long as it is there, then let it go as it passes away. If any thoughts bring feelings or emotions, pleasant or unpleasant, just note the strength and nature of these feelings and allow them to be as they are.

If you are repeatedly drawn into the drama of your thinking, bring your focus back to the belly and your breathing, as in the 'Mindful breathing' activity on page 27.

Try this

SEE ALSO

1 2 3 4 5 6 7 8
9 10 11 12 13 14
15 16 **17 18 19**
20 21 22 23 24
25 26 27 28 29
30 31 32 33 34
35 36 37 38 39
40 41 42 43 44
45 46 47 48 49

Chapter 4

REDUCE ANGER

Uncontrolled rage and anger are extremely destructive to our health, relationships, property and community. Our daily lives can often include so little 'down time' that stress levels creep up and up to the point where we literally 'boil over'. If you are someone with trauma or unresolved emotional difficulties from the past, you are also more likely to be at the mercy of uncontrolled anger. Whilst feeling angry at injustice or wrongdoing in the world can spur us forward to do something productive, uncontrolled outbursts of anger lead only downwards and, at their worst, can be life-threatening. This chapter explains what is going on in the brain when anger starts to rise and what we can do to prevent this happening. You can learn strategies to nip it the bud so that you just don't get to boiling point, and how to review and change how you react in anger-provoking situations. This will help you to keep your rational mind in charge of your life so you can live your life how you would like to, more of the time.

WAY 17

Don't flip your lid! Stay cool and calm

Learn how to work with mind science to stay in your right mind!

Although we think of ourselves as fairly evolved creatures, the truth is when we get worked up, we very quickly get 'emotionally hijacked (11) and our intelligence plummets. This leaves us as a slave to our primitive brains, which were in control back in the days when we were cave men!

Leading neurobiologist Dan Siegel (11) calls this emotional highjacking process 'flipping your lid'. He explains that, in very basic terms, **we have two parts to our brain**:

1. The old *primitive* part of our brain, the limbic system
This controls basic survival instincts, hunger, sexual desire and emotions. Because this part of our brain evolved at an early stage in human development, it is deep inside the brain.

2. The *intelligent* part of our brain, the cortex
This part of our brain evolved at a later stage in our development. It is responsible for intelligent and rational thinking, including problem-solving and strategic decision-making. It also performs the vital role of inhibiting and moderating the emotions and desires of the primitive 'cave man brain'. The cortex helps us, as civilised human beings, to operate in a complex modern world without being a total slave to our more basic desires. The cortex, being the 'newer part of the brain' covers the lymbic system, *like a lid* !

When we are relatively calm, going about our day-to-day business, both parts of the brain work in harmony, moderating our emotions and behaviour accordingly. However, when something really 'pushes our buttons', throwing us back in time to a past hurt or trauma, or touches a sensitive spot, the rational cortex becomes deactivated (flips off) and we are left in the control of our emotionally charged, 'caveman' brain, the limbic system. We literally 'flip our lid'!

In this emotionally charged, unchecked state, we can say and do things that in our usual rational state, we wouldn't dream of. It is a dangerous place to be and can be the cause of relationship breakdown, job losses, property destruction and at its worst, physical violence. Don't forget, we are in our most basic survival state at this time, often feeling that we are fighting for our lives, and with little intelligent thinking present to draw on.

The good news is that there is a way out! It takes effort, but it is possible to quickly 'flip our lid' back on when we feel ourselves becoming emotional. There are a number of strategies we can use to do this quickly and effectively (see **WAY 11: SOS strategies**, page 44). The key is to notice the process happening *early*. If you ignore the early warning signs and let the caveman brain take over, that's when you're in trouble and at a point of no return.

SEE ALSO
- **WAY 2: Switch off the stress response** (page 22)

Tune in to your early warning signs

How do you know you are starting to 'lose it'? Everyone has a physical reaction to the beginning of this process. Look at the diagram on page 22 which shows the physical symptoms which may be present as part of the stress response and which can kick in with heightened emotion, such as anger. Identify what your early warning sign is.

When you have identified what your body does to tell you that your lid is about to flip, WATCH OUT FOR IT! Don't let this sign go unchecked. For example, when your heart starts to pound, you need to act now! Try 7/11 breathing (see page 25)

and then divert your attention to doing something to get your adrenaline levels down. (See **WAY 11: SOS strategies**, page 44, for a list of emergency coping strategies, many of which are also covered in other parts of this guide).

Pick one and practise, practise, practise. This will help you to create a new response pathway for yourself, whereby as soon as you notice the stress response triggering, you can take immediate action to stop it taking over. This will increase your sense of control and your mental well-being.

Try this

WAY 18

Let go of anger – by getting tenser!

Use a powerful anti-tension technique to quickly reduce your anger level.

If you are prone to getting angry and you are trying to find a way of bringing down your levels of anger or tension, you may find trying to use some of the relaxation tips and breathing techniques described in this book somewhat challenging. This can be because you are unaware of the fact that the tension in your body is growing along with your anger. The key trick with many of the techniques in this book for managing stress and emotion is to become aware of the early signs of tension growing in the body. This is your indicator to move yourself away from growing emotional arousal.

However, if you are new to all of this, and have been used to feeling tense or angry for a long time, this can be a tall order! The following technique allows you to work with tension in the body and reduce it, by actually increasing it first! It is a good introduction to relaxation/ breathing techniques for beginners and a very helpful way of beginning to experience how it feels to be relaxed and free from tension, especially when we have forgotten what that feels like.

NOTE

This is not suitable for anyone who suffers with joint problems such as arthritis.

The tense and relax exercise explained

Squeeze your hands into fists, as tightly as possible. Really push the fingertips into your palms and squeeze the thumb over the fingers, so that your hands are screwed into tight balls. If you have very long fingernails and this is uncomfortable, you can clasp your hands together in front of you, interlocking your fingers.

Now, really focus on the tension you can feel building in your hands, feel it travelling up your wrists and into your forearms. Squeeze your forearms and elbows into the sides of your body and squeeze your shoulder blades together, so that now the whole of your upper body is tense, with all the muscles being squeezed hard. Hold for the count of five seconds and really focus on the sensations within your body. What does it feel like to have all this tension in your body? Now, slowly allow your muscles to begin to let go of that tension. Start at

your fingers, allowing them to gently unfold, then allow your wrists to relax, your arms to drop away from your sides and your shoulder blades to loosen and move apart again.

Focus on how free and loose and comfortable your muscles feel without tension. At this stage, you may like to imagine a favorite or calming colour sweeping over your body in a wave, from the head all the way down through the body to the toes.

Now repeat the process again as above. You will probably find that on the second round of letting tension go, you will feel even more relaxed!

You can also do this anywhere, with your arms at your side.

Try this

Tip: In an emergency situation, where you are worked up and need to calm down quickly, combine the above with 'walking away' (see **WAY 19: Get out of the boiling pot!**, page 66). Giving yourself some space and then quickly letting go of muscular tension will allow you much needed time to get your thinking head back on!

WAY 19

Get out of the boiling pot!

Learn to use a number 1 anger management technique.

As we saw in **WAY 17: Don't flip your lid!** once we recognise our anger warning signs, we MUST ACT! Expecting ourselves to stay in a situation which is highly provocative and remain calm and rational, is highly irrational! It just doesn't fit with how our brain works. Once the stress response is triggered, our whole central nervous system is geared up to fight or run away from the situation (**WAY 2: Switch off the stress response**, page 22). Trying to work against that instinct by staying in the situation and talking it out will only lead to disaster, as we have seen.

Number 1 anger management technique

The most effective anger management technique known to man is not rocket science! Here it is:

WALK AWAY!

When your buttons are pushed and you notice the physiological changes beginning to happen (as described in **WAY 17**), give yourself some space as quickly as you can. Obviously, if you are walking away from someone who may be further inflamed by your leaving, you need to briefly say that you are going in order to calm down to be able to talk properly. The other person needs to understand that you are not walking away because you don't think it's important, but really the opposite. Prepare a phrase that works for you, so that when you need to say it, it will come without you having to think too much (remember your thinking brain has shut down at this point!)

Give yourself at least 20 minutes. If you go off for 5 minutes, you will initially feel better but then as soon as you are back in the situation, your adrenaline levels will quickly rise again and you'll be back to square one! In that 20 minutes, ideally get some exercise, for example, take a brisk walk, jog on the spot, run up and down the stairs or use 7/11 breathing, all of which help you to calm down quickly. When you have calmed down a bit, you could also use the time to really put yourself in the other person's shoes. Ask yourself how would you feel in their situation?

SEE ALSO

• **WAY 37: See the other person's point of view** (page 110)

Tip: You could say something like:

'This is a really important issue and I want to talk about it properly, but I need to get 20 minutes time-out to calm down, then I will come back and discuss it with you.'

WAY 20 — Stand back from anger

Use the resources of the 'observing self'* to change old patterns of anger.

Anger, or indeed any intense, negative emotion, can be overwhelming. Even low levels can block rational thought, empathy and creative insight. In fact, it can lead us into a trance state, where we feel totally absorbed by it, and unable to see what is going on around us.

One way of breaking patterns of behaviour, arising from anger and other emotions, is to tap into our natural ability to step back from ourselves and see the bigger picture. This means using our observing self. In this mode of awareness, we can put distance between the emotion and our actions and see that we are much more than the anger, rage or jealousy. This helps us to understand how we may have become conditioned to react in certain ways, and to break the patterns which have unconsciously developed between our thoughts, emotions and certain situations and people.

In order to engage the observing self, we need to learn how to calm ourselves, using 7/11 breathing (see **WAY 2: Switch off the stress response**, page 22) or any of the relaxation techniques in **WAY 3: Take a mindful approach to relaxation**, page 26), **WAY 4: Practise the art of visualisation**, page 28), or **WAY 8: Create an anchor for calm**, page 38).

When we are relaxed, we can begin to move away from the kind of strong, negative self-talk going on in our heads, which we have used to build and justify our feelings of anger.

Through regular relaxation, we can also begin to see that there are other, more appropriate ways of meeting our emotional needs. Above all, when relaxation switches off the stress response (see **WAY 3**), we can take a step back and observe ourselves acting more resourcefully in difficult situations, as the following 'Try this' activity demonstrates.

SEE ALSO
- **WAY 4: Practise the art of visualisation** (page 28)
- *Chapter 3: Control Negative Thinking and Avoid Depression* (page 47)
- **'Create a soothing space'** in **WAY 22: Break the link between stress and ill-health** (page 74)

Tip: What are you saying to justify your anger, jealousy, etc? Would it stand up if put 'on trial'? What are your motivations to stop reacting in this emotional way?

Observe and realign your emotions

When you are relaxing, close your eyes and recall a time when you got angry or jealous towards someone, and imagine being in that scene. Begin to access some of those feelings.

Now imagine floating out of your body, for example, up to the ceiling or away to the side, and looking back at yourself from a distance. Notice something about your behaviour, for example, your facial expression, your body movements, the sound of your voice, that you may not have been aware of before.

Open your eyes, and spend a couple of minutes breathing slowly in and out from the belly area until you feel fully calm again. What was it you noticed about yourself when you got angry?

Consider how you would have liked to have behaved at that time. How would you like to have looked, moved, sounded, spoken? Build up as full a picture as you can.

Perhaps, you can draw on a past situation where you know that you behaved more resourcefully. Recall what you did and bring these things into the frame.

Close your eyes again and float back into the original scene, acting in your preferred way and noticing all the changes that occur in yourself, others' reactions, and the situation as a whole.

Open your eyes and notice how you can now think of that time and feel calmer. You have changed the associations between the situation and your emotions.

Finally, close your eyes and imagine a future, challenging situation and watch yourself staying calm and acting in this new way. Float into yourself and notice all the positive changes in how you feel. This will help to embed the new associations.

1 2 3 4 5 6 7 8
9 10 11 12 13 14
15 16 17 18 19
20 **21 22 23 24**
25 26 27 28 29
30 31 32 33 34
35 36 37 38 39
40 41 42 43 44
45 46 47 48 49

Chapter 5

IMPROVE PHYSICAL HEALTH AND SLEEP

There is a growing body of research which demonstrates the interconnections between the brain, behaviour, immunity and health. For example, how we use our minds, including our thoughts, expectations and how we interpret life's events, can greatly impact upon our body's cellular activity and immunity and a whole host of physiological functions (12). This chapter will help you learn ways of creating an image of wellness and reducing the harmful effects of stress by 'self-soothing'. Pain has a strong psychological element, so you can practise ways of reducing pain and discomfort. You can also foster positive expectations about medical treatment and your body's ability to heal.

Sleep is often disturbed by stress and we develop unhelpful patterns of behaviour which can make it difficult to get deep rest at night. This chapter also includes tips on sleep hygiene and ways of changing thoughts and feelings around sleep. Finally, you can learn how to use the natural dream state to get off to a good night's sleep.

WAY 21 Think well, be well

Use the mind–body connection to improve your health and vitality.

The strong connection between our mind and our body is easily demonstrated by thinking about eating a lemon. Notice how quickly your mouth begins to pucker and fill with saliva, although there is no lemon there, or how, when you remember a very embarrassing time, you might find yourself blushing, even though you are only thinking about the past. Dr Robert Ader was a founder of the field of psychoneuroimmunology (PNI)*, which has demonstrated communication pathways between our mind (thoughts, expectation and the way we perceive life's events), our brain, hormones, immunity and disease (12). While worry, despair and negative beliefs about our health or the treatment we are receiving can lead to poor health outcomes, for example, lowered immunity and slower wound healing, the reverse is equally valid. We can use the way we think and what we believe to enhance our health and immunity, whether for boosting our energy levels, recovering from injury or surgery, alleviating the symptoms of particular conditions, reducing the side effects from medication (see **WAY 24: Expect the best treatment**, page 78), increasing the number and activity of disease-fighting T-cells, or lowering levels of stress hormones and blood pressure.

When we want to improve our health or energy, we can create a powerful visualisation of ourselves as full of wellness, following the guidelines for visualisation in **WAY 4: Practise the art of visualisation**. What do we look like? How do we move? What do we sound like when we speak? For example, we might imagine ourselves with a smiling face, feel ourselves moving with vigour, saying a bright 'Good morning' to people we meet.

As we relax into our imagined state of wellness, the body will react as if we are experiencing these sensations for real (just as we produced saliva at the thought of that lemon). We might also visualise life after recovery from injury, illness or surgery, doing all those things we look forward to doing. Again, we can see ourselves full of life and good energy, notice what it feels like when we swim, or run, return to our hobbies or play with our grandchildren.

We know that exercise is good for our health as it stimulates the production of 'feel good' brain chemicals, called endorphins, in our bodies, and also provides an outlet for high circulating levels of stress hormones caused by anxiety. Even while we may not be able to exercise, visualising doing it will stimulate the same neural connections and bring benefits to our physical well-being. If you find this difficult to do, remember a time when you were physically active. What did it feel like? 'Bathe' yourself in those memories and sensations.

SEE ALSO
- **WAY 4: Practise the art of visualisation** (page 28)
- **WAY 46: Cultivate optimism** (page 134)

Our emotional response to illness can have a crucial bearing on our recovery and future health (13). When we are unwell, it is important to separate the illness from our core identity. Talking about 'my migraine', 'my arthritis', 'my cancer' or 'my heart disease' allows our condition to define who we are. In addition, focusing on our symptoms helps to maintain them (see **WAY 5: What you focus on is what you get**, page 30). Instead, we can ensure that we continue to take control of the smaller things in our life and meet our human needs for fulfilment (see **WAY 1: Bulletproof your happiness**, page 20).

Create an image of wellness

Take some time to relax. In your mind, consider the following statement: 'When I think of myself as full of wellness and strength, I am like a ...' Allow an image to emerge. An example might be a strong tree, deeply rooted in the earth but spreading and reaching upwards into the sky. You might base your image on an interest you have, for example, as a surfer, riding a huge, shining wave. Keep returning to your image whenever you are relaxing, adding more detail as it emerges. You can then begin to access it when you are feeling anxious or worried, tired or down, or when you are about to go into a challenging situation. Notice the positive effect it has on your mind and body.

Try this

Tip: While deeply relaxed, ask yourself, 'What has that "well me" in the future done to feel better?' Your unconscious mind will have some answers and these may pop up in the moment or at some time afterwards. Take notice.

WAY 22

Break the link between stress and ill-health

Reduce stress and prompt healing with metaphors for self-soothing.

Stress adversely affects both our behaviour and our physical health. Stress and anxiety may prompt us into a host of unhealthy behaviours, for example, smoking, taking harmful drugs, eating the wrong foods, indulging in sexually risky behaviour, avoiding exercise, driving too fast, and so on. Many health problems have psychological elements and may be exacerbated by stress or even triggered by stress, including skin conditions, allergies, digestive complaints, high blood pressure, migraine, cardiac illness and auto-immune diseases like cancer and ME.

When we are anxious or worried we trigger the stress response* (see **WAY 2: Switch off the stress response**, page 22) and the body produces stress hormones. What evolved to save our lives in real danger may now make us ill. As the stress hormones remain in our system long-term, many of our normal, health-giving functions are suppressed and this can lead to a host of physical and mental problems, including raised blood pressure, shallow breathing, lowered energy and sex drive, suppressed immune response, poor digestion, disrupted sleep and 'fuzzy' thinking.

Finding ways of reducing stress in our lives prevents this vicious cycle occurring. This book contains many ways of avoiding and lowering stress, starting with some of the basics included in Chapters 1 and 2, and moving on to challenging negative thinking (Chapter 3), reducing anger (Chapter 4) and setting achievable goals for doing the things you enjoy (Chapter 6).

When we experience physical health problems, we can learn to harness the power of the mind to 'self-soothe', where we deeply relax and allow our minds to create healing metaphors* for our well-being, illness, symptoms or discomfort. We all use metaphors to describe our physical condition. For example, we may talk about pain using words like 'burning', 'stabbing' 'dull' or 'nagging'.

We can utilise these same metaphors as a key to creating new ones which are self-soothing and healing. We could imagine a cool liquid bathing an affected part of our body to soothe away 'burning' sensations, or a coloured light flowing into an area of 'dull' discomfort. The metaphor engages the imaginative right hemisphere of the brain and bypasses the conscious, rational part of our mind, which may be negative or resistant. In this way, it 'speaks' to the unconscious, where we can try out a new way of seeing the world and new patterns of responding. This process has been utilised by hypnotherapists with

Tip: Identify some of the metaphors you use to describe your physical condition, symptoms or discomfort, including words, shapes, colours, sounds etc. Then move on to the 'Try this' activity opposite.

Create a soothing space

Follow the guidelines in the 'Try this' **'Staircase to relaxation'** activity on page 29 but visualise a place which is particularly healing and soothing. Imagine that this place has everything you need for soothing any physical difficulties you are experiencing. Using the metaphors you have identified (above), allow your mind to come up with healing sounds, colours, textures and other qualities as antidotes to these. Your space might include particular features, for example, a bright waterfall or shower to wash away a 'heavy weight' of fatigue or 'black blobs' of unhealthy cells; a shaft of sunlight to warm and invigorate the 'icy pool' of poor circulation, or a pile of soft cushions to absorb 'stabbing' pain.

Allow these things to emerge as you drift comfortably in deep rest. Visualise your physical health being transformed in this place and what this feels like, for example, energy flowing through the body, skin feeling smooth and intact, an unwanted growth shrinking, an organ functioning well. When you are ready to leave your healing space, imagine returning up the stairs and come back into full consciousness.

You can also use this exercise to create metaphors for, and transform, difficult emotions such as worry, fear or anger.

Try this

---

excellent results in reducing symptoms in certain conditions which are difficult to treat, such as irritable bowel syndrome (14).

We can elaborate our metaphors into healing stories, for example, imagining our immune system as a castle that needs defending, and the guards doing their job well; or our high blood pressure as a narrow river which needs unblocking from weeds, rocks and silt, so that it can widen and flow more quietly and smoothly. Milton H. Erickson, the American psychiatrist who pioneered innovative approaches to clinical hypnotherapy, was a great story-teller and used stories to reframe* his patients' experiences of illness and pain (15).

Self-soothing can also help us to think more calmly and rationally about the health-related decisions we take in our lives and the choices we make about our lifestyles.

SEE ALSO
- **WAY 4: Practise the art of visualisation** (page 28)
- **'Create an image of wellness'** in **WAY 21: Think well, be well** (page 73)

WAY 23 Turn down that pain

We can learn to diminish our experience of pain with some simple mind techniques.

All pain has a psychological element. We know that pain and other distressing bodily sensations, for example, tinnitus or skin irritation, can seem much worse when we focus on them, or when we are anxious, stressed or depressed. In fact, pain seems to put us into *trance*, narrowing our focus of attention so that the experience is heightened and all-consuming. This makes it difficult to consciously divert away to more pleasant things.

The 'gate control' theory of pain (16) suggests that pain signals compete with other signals as they reach the spinal cord and can be switched on or off depending on the priority of other messages. A well known example is our natural impulse to shout or jump up and down when we stub a toe, rather than just stand still and focus on the pain. Pain that accompanies safe and pleasant experiences may be classified as irrelevant and never reach the brain. This suggests that getting absorbed in what we enjoy can help to block our awareness of pain. When someone is in pain, the emotional brain is activated and,

as we saw in Chapters 3 and 4, they may be prone to inflexible, 'black-and-white', 'all or nothing' thinking in relation to their experience. Many of the techniques introduced in Chapter 3 for breaking down or challenging this style of thinking may be helpful.

Learning to stay relaxed is the first step to diminishing the hold painful or unpleasant sensations can have on our consciousness (see **WAY 2: Switch off the stress response**, page 22, **WAY 3: Take a mindful approach to relaxation**, page 26, **WAY 4: Practise the art of visualisation**, page 28 and **WAY 8: Create an anchor for calm**, page 38). We can then begin to focus on pleasant events and sensations to distract us away from pain (see **WAY 11: SOS strategies**, page 44). Laughter is a wonderful, natural medicine for pain, increasing levels of serotonin (the 'happy chemical') in the brain and diminishing anxiety and stress related to the experience of pain.

The mind has the ability to change or reduce physical sensation. The American psychiatrist and clinical hypnotherapist Milton H. Erickson, clearly demonstrated the importance of suggestion and expectation in the experience of pain (15) (see also **WAY 24: Expect the best treatment**, page 78). As a result of his work and those of hypnotherapists working in the field of pain, we know that we can learn to alter pain into less disturbing sensations like tingling or

Tip: When you are experiencing pain or discomfort, grade its intensity from 0% (not present at all) to 100% (as bad as you could possibly imagine). Grading or *scaling* pain in this way engages the thinking mind, distracting away from the emotional overwhelm of the experience. It also enables you to notice finer distinctions and improvements from day to day.

warmth, using self-soothing metaphors (see **WAY 22: Break the link between stress and ill-health**, page 74), or use our minds to 'turn down' the pain. This helps to give us back a sense of control, which is important in avoiding anxiety, negative thinking and depression.

When we feel disassociated from something, we feel less emotional about it. You can distance yourself from pain by imagining you are far away from it, in another room, or another place, or even 'outside of yourself'

and thereby free of pain. This can be helpful for long-term, chronic pain.

NOTE
Always see a doctor about any pain you are experiencing before undertaking any pain relief activity.

SEE ALSO
- **WAY 15: Beat the blues** (page 54)
- **'Create a soothing space' in WAY 22: Break the link between stress and ill-health** (page 74)

Turn down that pain

Relax deeply using the staircase induction method in **WAY 4: Practise the art of visualisation**, page 28.

When you reach the bottom of the staircase, imagine yourself in some sort of control room. Ahead of you is a panel of dials and switches. Notice that there is a large dial for pain control and notice its size, shape and texture. Around the dial are numbers from 0 to 20, each number marked with a notch in the dial. Now hold the dial and notice the feel of it under your hand.

Begin to turn the dial down notch by notch, starting at 20. Before turning down a notch, take a deep breath in, and as you turn the dial, take a long, slow out-breath.

Notice the sense of relaxation in your body. Turn the dial down to a point which seems right for you.

Once you have reached this point, imagine floating into a place of deep relaxation. Enjoy the sights, sounds and other sensations in this place until it is time to return to your day.

At another time, experiment with other dials or controls which are in your control room and which are there to increase feelings of calm, comfort or healing. Imagine adjusting these in a positive or upwards direction.

Try this

WAY 24 Expect the best treatment

Manage your beliefs and expectations to get the best from medical treatment.

The placebo* effect is a well-researched phenomenon, showing that positive expectations by both patient and health care provider can positively affect health outcomes. Our minds are enormously susceptible to suggestion and the power of our beliefs. When we believe that a particular treatment will be beneficial, or when a physician seems confident and concerned, our bodies are more likely to respond favourably, even in the case of 'sugar pills' which contain no active substances. In fact, sugar pills have been found to cause profound changes in the same area of the brain as the drugs they are masquerading as. The active ingredient seems to be the *power of belief* that the patients have received a powerful and effective treatment. For example, research has shown that a placebo given by injection is more effective than if given by a tablet, because the injection is seen as stronger medicine (17).

In the same way as positive expectations can enhance the effects of our treatment, patients who expect the worst health-wise tend to get just that. Factors which feed our negative expectations can lead to a negative or *nocebo** effect. Examples include believing that you are prone to a particular disease, being told by the physician that you will experience particular side-effects from a drug or that a procedure will hurt, or noticing a look of doubt on the doctor's face when she is talking about the low risk of a given procedure. At its very worst, there are many anecdotal reports of patients being told they have three or six months to live and dying 'dutifully' on the final day of their prescribed time span.

SEE ALSO
• **WAY 5: What you focus on is what you get** (page 30)

Tip: Cultivate feelings of gratitude towards your health care givers, your medicine or the surgical procedure you are about to have. Feelings of deep gratitude create positive expectations and prime our bodies to respond to the benefits of what is being offered.

The inner smile

Close your eyes and imagine them smiling down into your body. 'Smile' into each part of your body, working down from your head, neck and chest, through each organ, through your arms and hands, down the back, legs and into the feet. Imagine each part of the body smiling back.

If you have a particular part of the body which is painful or is not functioning as

it should, spend more time smiling into the area.

This practice increases endorphins (feel-good chemicals) in the body which support immunity and optimism and are the body's natural pain killers.

WAY 25 Clean up your sleep act

Learn some sleep hygiene techniques to sleep naturally and restfully.

Sleep is an entirely natural process, one that we didn't even have to think about when we were babies or children. However, our busy adult lives can raise our levels of stress to an extent where we start to worry about sleep. At night our continued thinking can stimulate our waking minds into mental activity, whether problem-solving, list-making or anxious imaginings. In fact, many of us do all sorts of things to 'try' to get to sleep, rather than getting our conscious minds 'out of the way' so that we can allow sleep to take over.

Many of the difficulties we regularly experience in living, including difficulty in sleeping, arise from the patterns of thinking and behaviours we have learned, however unintentionally and consciously. For example, we may regularly postpone going to bed because we are channel-hopping on the TV or playing computer games. If sleep has become a problem, we may think about going upstairs or getting ready for bed with anxiety or even dread. Using a 'sleep hygiene' approach can start to change unhelpful patterns and stimulate thinking and activities which pave the way for a good night's sleep.

'SLEEPY MIND' CHECKLIST

- Avoid stimulating activities an hour before bedtime, such as watching TV, playing computer games, surfing the Internet. Minimise persistent worrying by keeping a notebook of worry 'topics' which you can write in at any time (see also **WAY 10: Put worry in its place**, page 42).
- Try to instil a routine around bedtime and getting-up time.
- If you wake in the night, avoid turning the light on or looking at the time. Focus on your breath or on relaxing the body, starting from the feet and working up to the head.
- If you don't get back to sleep within about 30 minutes, get up and sit in a cool, dark room. If you must do something, make sure it is a boring, non-stimulating activity, rather than something you enjoy. As soon as you are really tired, leave the task and return to bed. Focus on your breathing or body relaxation again.
- If you are still awake after another 20–30 minutes, get up and do another boring task or pick up the one you left. Once your mind realises that it will be punished for not sleeping (rather than rewarded), it will learn to get you off to sleep at night!

You also may need to look at physical factors which might be affecting your sleep, like alcohol, caffeine, timing of meals and exercise, body heat, and hormonal imbalance. The CBT approach used in the exercise opposite looks at thoughts, actions and feelings and can help to change your responses towards going to bed.

SEE ALSO
- **WAY 26: Dream yourself into sleep** (page 82)
- *Chapter 1: Lay the Foundations of Well-being – Some mind science basics* (page 19)
- *Chapter 3: Control Negative Thinking and Avoid Depression* (page 47)

Changing patterns

On a piece of paper, draw three columns, headed 'Action', 'Thoughts' and 'Feelings'. Work out the usual steps you take to get to bed, starting around one hour before. Number each step and alongside it, write down a typical thought you might have at that time, and an accompanying feeling. For example, one step might be:

Action	Thoughts	Feelings
Turn off TV at the end of the evening.	'Here comes another bad night's sleep.'	Anxiety about not being able to function at work tomorrow.

When you have written these steps down, consider how you might change the actions, using some of the ideas opposite. Write these down in order. Alongside each, come up with a more positive thought to counter the old, negative way of thinking, and imagine how you might feel as a result. Here is an example:

Action	Thoughts	Feelings
Have a nice, warm bath an hour before bedtime.	'I am helping myself to relax.'	Feeling relaxed and a bit sleepy.

Try this

Work out all the steps that will take you naturally into sleep, along with accompanying thoughts and feelings. When relaxed, see yourself going through these steps, as if you were watching yourself on a TV screen. Notice how calm and increasingly sleepy you look. When you have watched yourself going through all the steps, float into yourself on that screen and go through them again, this time noticing how you feel.

Tip: Make your bedroom a place you associate with sleep. If possible, remove the TV, computer, office or studying area to another room. Control lighting and noise by using an eye mask or ear plugs if necessary. You can also interrupt the usual bedtime patterns and associations by doing your bedtime reading, sleeping or washing in a different place, or rearranging your bedroom.

NOTE

If sleep is a persistent problem, see your GP to rule out underlying health problems, and for assessment and advice.

WAY 26 Dream yourself into sleep

Use self-hypnosis to train the mind to get off to sleep.

Sleeping is not about 'switching off' the brain, but rather, activating it in a different way. When we have difficulty in sleeping, it is often because we are disturbed by the external sounds and sensations and try to block them out. However, we can use the sounds and other features around us to encourage the natural 'auto symbolic affect'. This occurs as our attention begins to turn inwards and sensory input from the outside starts getting altered into fragments of dreams. For example, the sound of a dripping tap might symbolically become a running stream, or the warmth of the bedclothes might become the feel of sunshine on a holiday beach. These visualisations help us to drift into trance or sleep.

Tip: The more practised you become at relaxing, the more easily you will drift into sleep and the deeper your sleep will be. Use the relaxation techniques in **WAY 3: Take a mindful approach to relaxation** (page 26) and **WAY 4: Practise the art of visualisation** (page 28) to take a short, deep rest during the day. This will boost your energy for the rest of the day and prepare the ground for getting off to sleep at night.

Three things to take you into sleep

Practise the following steps to dream yourself off to sleep. They will utilise the 'chattering mind' and its tendency to jump about in order to create a dreamy state:

- With eyes open, find a spot in the room to focus on. Even if it is dark, train your focus on one small part of your field of sight. Really concentrate on this point for a while, and then close your eyes. Imagine bringing this point closer to you and 'see' its characteristics – its colour, texture, and so on, then let it go.

- Open your eyes again and find three points around your original point of focus, which are in your field of vision, while concentrating again on the original point. 'Hold' these points in your focus for a few moments, and then let them go. Close your eyes.

- Bring to your awareness three sounds in your surroundings, which might include sounds outside the room, sounds inside the room, and even sounds inside your body like your breathing. Spend a few moments focusing on each, then let them go.

- Bring to your awareness three feelings. These might include the warmth or weight of the bed covers on your body, the air on your face or an internal sensation. Focus on each in turn, and then let them go.

- Now imagine three relaxing or absorbing sights – a sunset, a tranquil lake, a colourful parade – and stay with your images in turn, for a few moments.

- Next, imagine three relaxing or absorbing sounds – a steam train, a piece of music, a fountain – and stay with these sounds in turn, for a few moments.

- Next, imagine three pleasing sensations – slipping into a warm bath, walking across soft grass, sailing in a yacht – and stay with these feelings, in turn, for a while.

- Continue to cycle between imagining three new, relaxing sights, three new sounds and three new sensations until you slip into sleep.

1 2 3 4 5 6 7 8
9 10 11 12 13 14
15 16 17 18 19
20 21 22 23 24
25 26 **27 28 29
30** 31 32 33 34
35 36 37 38 39
40 41 42 43 44
45 46 47 48 49

Chapter 6

SET GOALS AND BOOST YOUR MOTIVATION

How often have you felt the frustration of promising yourself that you *will* make a change, whether starting a new routine or achieving something important to you, only to find yourself a few months down the line having not achieved those things, *again*? Our basic human need to feel in control of our lives, to learn and feel challenged, and have a sense of achievement are all assaulted by this sense of failure. If it is continually repeated, life can start to feel 'stuck', empty or even meaningless. It is for this important reason that we have devoted this chapter to achieving goals. In this chapter you will find an opportunity to stand back and refocus on what is important in your life. You can then learn how to set realistic and achievable goals and, most importantly, how to motivate yourself to achieve them. Rather than floating aimlessly through life, you will have gained some practical skills to begin moving in just the right direction for you.

WAY 27 Refocus on your life goals

Tune in to what REALLY matters to you.

It is so easy to get caught up in the busyness of day-to-day life that sometimes we can lose sight of the bigger picture and what our most important goals are. This exercise can help you refocus on what is REALLY important to you. It can draw you back to your core beliefs and values and help you bring things into your life that really matter. It can also help you to let go of what's using up your time and energy without being of any real value to you.

> **Tip:** If you need help creating goals which work, follow: **WAY 28: Set realistic goals** (page 88), **WAY 29: Keep goals SMART** (page 90), and **WAY 30: Get up and go – achieve your goals at last!** (page 92).

Write your own eulogy

Imagine your grave stone! If your family, friends and colleagues were asked to write on it what they thought about you when you were living, what would you want them to write? If it commemorated your proudest achievements, what would you want them to be?

Draw this shape on a sheet of paper and write your responses down on the gravestone. Here's an example:

RIP

Kind

Patient

Marathon runner

Owned own business

Loyal friend

Open-minded

Now, think for a moment about what might be on your gravestone if you continue living your life in exactly the same way as you are now?

Would you want the way you are currently living your life to be reflected on the stone, just as it is now?

Are there things that you know you are doing too much of, which are not a good use of your resources, time and energy? For instance, do you spend too much time making sure the house is immaculate whilst ignoring or even shouting at the kids? Do you spend too much money on alcohol, which you could be saving for that round-the-world trip you have always longed for? Remember what they say: '*This is it, life is not a dress rehearsal!*'

So, now get practical: what specific changes do you need to make in order to have the eulogy you would be proud of?

Examples might be:
- Find a cleaner and take the kids out to the park while they clean.
- Save £10 a week towards my big trip.
- Spend 5 minutes a day meditating in order to be calmer and more patient.

Try this

WAY 28 Set realistic goals

Learn to 'chunk' goals in order to finally achieve them.

The number one biggest mistake we can make when trying to bring positive change into our lives is to make our goals too big, or to set too many of them, so that we inevitably feel overwhelmed and don't do anything.

Here's a technique that can help you to prioritise and break down your goals so that you have a clear beginning and end point, rather than getting lost in the process and giving up. It uses the NLP concept of 'chunking down', ie. moving from the general to the specific. In this case, you can try breaking a big goal into smaller, more precise 'chunks' so that it becomes manageable and achievable.

SEE ALSO
• **WAY 29: Keep goals SMART** (page 90)

Get it all down on paper

First, write a list of the things you really want to change or achieve in life. Just write down anything you have been thinking about, all the 'to do' stuff in your head that you feel you never get to attend to and which just builds stress. Writing everything down means you are taking a step towards addressing it. Don't feel there should be any order to the list at this point, just get it all down. So, your list could look something like this:

When you have your list, prioritise the items, just by writing a number next to each one to show its level of urgency or importance to you right now.

This might come very easily to you if you know what your goals are. If you are not so sure (but know things aren't right), try using the list of emotional needs on page 21. By setting goals in each of those areas, you will know that you are well on your way to feeling happier, as these needs are essential for our emotional well-being. For example:

TO DO...

Sort the garden out
Bag up my unused clothes for charity
Finish the report for work
Write a letter to my son's school
Phone the mortgage company
Book Grandma's birthday weekend away
Get car MOT

TO DO...

Sort the garden out 7
Bag up my unused clothes for charity 6
Finish the report for work 5
Write a letter to my son's school ②
Phone the mortgage company 4
Book Grandma's birthday weekend away ③
Get car MOT ①

Then for each of the top three items, 'chunk' it down into the steps you need to complete each one. For some of them, this might involve just one or two steps, for others, there might be more. Most importantly, write down when you can realistically do each step. Be as specific as possible, for example, rather than writing 'today', or next week, write down both the day and the specific point in that day. It's better to use 'points' in your day, for example, 'during lunchbreak' or 'when I get back from work' rather than clock time, as times can pass and then you might feel like you've lost the opportunity. Remember to make each step small, so it's achievable.

For example:

TO DO...

1 Get car MOT
  Find company on internet, call them
  to book it. (today when baby naps)

2 Write a letter to the school
  Call school, find out who I write the
  letter to (at lunchtime, while kids eat)
  Write it (tonight after kids are in bed,
  before dinner)

When you've completed the first three tasks, then go on and prioritise the next three, following the same pattern of breaking down the task and making each small task time specific. This is such an important point, so that when you set yourself very small achievable tasks you do start completing them, which increases your motivation. See the '5 minute rule' on page 93 for more tips on motivation.

Try this

Tip: If you feel that three goals are too many to start with and it's putting you off starting, just do one, get that completed, then move on to the next. Each time you tick a task off, you'll find the next step easier!

WAY 29 Keep goals SMART

Discover an easy way to really help you meet your goals.

There is an art to setting goals. Approaching it in a haphazard way seldom works. If this was not true we would all be slimmer, fitter, have given up drinking/smoking, taken up new hobbies and started that business! How many coffee room conversations start, 'I really must...'?

If you learn to use effective techniques for setting goals, life really does become more fulfilling, as you get a sense of moving forward and achieving things, rather than a sense of staying stuck, which can make life dull and uninteresting.

If you structure your goals in a certain way, you have far more chance of achieving them. This then increases your energy to continue setting more goals and life moves on in the way you really want it to.

Contrast this to just being swept along and reacting to what life throws at us. When we feel in control of our lives, we are at our happiest (1). Setting and achieving goals gives us a great sense of being in control.

Tip: Remember, that at first you might need to write goals down in this structured way but soon, as with learning any new skills, the process will start to feel more natural and you will find that you can achieve more and more.

Smarten up your goals

Use this acronym to shape your goals and hugely increase your chance of achieving them: **SMART**

S = Specific
Make sure you narrow down what it is you want to achieve.

M = Measurable
How will you know when you have achieved what it is you have set out to achieve?

A = Attainable
Make sure the goal is something within your reach, not something you have to wait for or don't have the resources at present to realise.

R = Realistic
Don't make the goal too difficult. If anything, make it too easy, then when you achieve it, you have an increased sense of your abilities and more confidence to set and achieve more complex goals.

T = Time related
Put a time frame on your goal of when you will achieve it, rather than leaving it open ended. This will give you a deadline to work to, so that you don't just leave it and think you will get round to it at some point.

So, here is an example:

You need to get fit. You've tried the gym and hated it. You used to enjoy badminton but don't have anyone to play with. Instead of waiting for a partner to drop in your lap, you decide it's time to take action and find one.

Specific: To find a partner to play with once a week for an hour, at either of the two closest venues to me.

Measurable: I will have achieved it when I am playing badminton once a week.

Attainable: I will put notices up at those two venues, as I know I can get to either one easily. I will also call both of them to see if they have any lessons or leagues I can join.

Realistic: I will play just once a week as I know I can manage that.

Time related: I will drop the notices in on Saturday morning and I will call both clubs by the end of this week.

You are now well on your way to increasing your fitness!

Try this

30

Get up and go – achieve your goals at last!

Find out how to avoid getting stuck and to start getting things done.

Are there any New Year's resolutions you haven't got around to yet?

Why is it that, although we have all the very best intentions of making positive changes in our lives, ones that will be of enormous benefit, somehow these changes just never seem to happen?

One big unknown around setting and achieving goals is this:

When there is WILL and EMOTION in conflict, EMOTION always wins! (18)

Here's an example of how this works in day-to-day life. You know you really need to start doing some exercise. Your doctor has told you that your weight is really becoming a problem (you're officially 'obese!'), your spouse has started tennis again and you feel guilty about that. When you do walk uphill, you notice your breathing becomes laboured and you feel a bit dizzy. However, when you get home from work each night and it's cold and dark, you sit in the sofa feeling cosy and relaxed and the thought of getting up and out to the gym is very unattractive. You then decide that you'll just stay in tonight but definitely go tomorrow... You know that you should go tonight (will) but you just don't feel like it (emotion).

So, this is where we get stuck! The trick is to stop waiting to feel like doing it and to accept that this is just not going to happen. Every top athlete will tell you that often the way they get themselves out to train is by forcing themselves to do it. This doesn't sound very appealing, but the 'Try this' activity opposite is a trick that will will really help.

Tip: See **WAY 5: What you focus on is what you get** (page 30) to get further ideas for motivating yourself.

Overcoming stuckness – the 5 minute rule!

When you have a task which you know you need to do but just don't feel like doing, make it easy on yourself. Recognising that your will and emotions will be in conflict, make a deal with yourself that you will only do the task for five minutes. Suddenly, it seems a lot less daunting: it's only five minutes after all!

In all likelihood, once you have done five minutes, you will have bypassed your resistance and be in flow* with the activity so that you want to carry on (see **WAY 48: Get into flow**, page 138).

However, just in case you don't, you have still achieved five minutes of the activity, which is better than doing nothing, and a step in the right direction.

Chapter 7

ENHANCE YOUR ASSERTIVENESS, SELF-ESTEEM AND CONFIDENCE

There is a wealth of self-help material available for people who feel lacking in self-esteem and confidence, which is perhaps an indication of what a common complaint this is. Trying to feel better about ourselves can prompt us to go down all sorts of unhelpful avenues and sometimes this can lead to unhealthy or destructive habits, which we address in Chapter 9. This chapter will help you take effective steps to becoming a more confident person, starting by cultivating a sense of achievement, which meets an important emotional need in all of us. It goes on to distil some of the best, evidence-based techniques and tools around, providing a practical guide to feeling better about yourself and behaving more assertively. Acting confidently, setting boundaries and saying what you mean may feel unfamiliar and challenging. Don't worry, there are tips along the way that will help you take the plunge and then follow easy steps to becoming a more confident person.

Boost your self-esteem

How meeting one specific emotional need can impact positively on how you feel about yourself.

Generally in life our self-esteem will ebb and flow. Sometimes we can feel we have little control over this, that somehow these fluctuations 'just happen.' However, this is rarely the case!

When our self-esteem dips, it may well be that someone said something, or that something happened which triggered a memory or pattern from the past. These memories or patterns are often stored unconsciously, ie they are not at the forefront of our minds. This means that we may not even be aware of them being triggered by a current event, we just have a sense of feeling OK, then not feeling OK.

Our baseline of how we generally feel about ourselves does stem largely from the early messages we receive in life. If you know that these were very negative over a long period of time, you may benefit from one-to-one therapy to help let go of them and move on with your life.

However, there is one key skill to boosting our self-esteem and keeping it at a generally higher level, so that when things come along that may have previously floored us, we can keep our head above water and still feel OK. This skill is linked to our emotional need of having a sense of achievement.

We all need to ensure that we have a range of activities in our lives that we find stimulating, and that give us a sense of satisfaction when we complete them. This can be anything from playing a musical instrument, supporting a friend in a time of trouble, having a satisfying job, or being able to arrange a vase of flowers beautifully! It really doesn't matter what it is, but there is truth in the saying, 'We are what

SEE ALSO
- **WAY 46: Cultivate optimism** (page 134)
- **WAY 48: Get into flow** (page 138)

Tip: It may also be useful to think of some 'emergency activities', things that you can do if you have a sense of your mood dropping or negative thoughts creeping in. Remember that it is at these times that you need these activities more than ever. Because it can be very hard to 'think' of possibilities at a time when you feel stressed or low, having a list ready to go can really help to get yourself back on track.

Make sure the emergency activities you list are easy to achieve and are things you enjoy. It can help to have them written on a small card to keep in your wallet or have them stuck up somewhere so that they are visible when you need them.

Take practical steps to better self-esteem

Make a list of activities which you know give you a sense of achievement. Think widely and think 'achievable'. The list should ideally include some activities that you are doing on an ongoing basis, like a job or hobby. Ask yourself the following:

- Do you get a sense of achievement from your job or main activity?

- If the answer is no, are there aspects of it that you derive a sense of achievement from?

- Is there scope for you to build on those aspects or pursue an alternative job or interest which has more of those aspects?

Most people rely on their job or main activity to obtain a sense of achievement. However, if you are in a situation where it is currently very difficult to change your main occupation or activity (eg. you are currently unable to find another job, or you are a sole carer) and you do not derive a sense of achievement from what you are doing, it is essential to find other ways to meet this vital need. You might pick up old hobbies, even if only for an hour a week. You might start reading a book about a subject that interests you, do some baking or write a letter to a friend you haven't been in contact with. The list is endless but bringing a small sense of achievement into your life will make a difference.

Being mindful of your need to feel you are achieving things in life means that you can be on the lookout for opportunities (see **Way 5: What you focus on is what you get**, page 30). Notice how you feel stronger, 'taller' or more complete when you have achieved something.

WAY 32 'Fake it till you make it'

It's the ultimate confidence trick - learn to increase your self-confidence just by acting!

One of the most commonly reported psychological complaints is feeling a lack of confidence. Janice Davies, who specialises in the study of self-confidence and is known as 'The Attitude Specialist', has found that 95 per cent of children and adults report feeling a lack of confidence at some point in their lives. Richard Lovelace, a psychotherapist, found that low confidence and self-esteem is closely linked to how we deal with stress (20), in that if we are suffering from low self-esteem, we will also find life's challenges harder to deal with. It is, of course, the case that some people have had a start in life which has made them feel fundamentally secure and confident. However, it is surprising how many of us who present as very confident, often feel shy and nervous on the inside!

While confidence levels can be significantly affected by our early parenting experiences (and the messages about our worth we received as small children), it is also true to say that they are not set in stone. There is plenty we can do as adults to dramatically increase our self-confidence.

We have already seen in **WAY 31: Boost your self-esteem**, that a very important factor in maintaining self-esteem comes from engaging in activities which you can gain a sense of achievement from. One additional, powerful technique for developing confidence is based on the old saying, 'Fake it till you make it!'. As long ago as 1894, the philosopher, William James, pronounced that:

'If you want a quality, act as if you already have it'.

Plenty of research since has shown that acting 'as if' you feel a particular way, including confident, leads to you really feeling that way (21). The following activity, based on this premise, is particularly helpful when you know you have an event coming up which you feel nervous about and know you need a confidence boost.

Tip: Don't forget that, with practice, new, confident ways will start to become naturally part of how you are. They won't feel fake for long, they will start to feel *part of you*.

Borrow someone else's confidence!

First, think of a person who you perceive as being confident. This might be a celebrity, a friend or colleague. It really doesn't matter who they are, just as long as you can picture them well, including how they might conduct themselves in different situations.

Then, think about what it is about them that makes you think they are confident. You might like to consider the following categories:

Non-verbal – How do they stand/hold themselves, what do they do with their hands, what kind of facial expression do they have, what kind of distance do they leave between themselves and others when conversing?

Verbal – What is their tone of voice like? How do they pace what they say? What type of language do they use? What is the volume of their voice like?

Appearance – How do they groom themselves, eg. hair, make-up, what type of clothes and accessories do they wear? Now, from the above, take whatever it is you want to borrow! Of course, you don't want to end up a carbon copy of someone else, just pick what it is about that person which you think would be useful for you. It might help to write these down.

It may be that you think about a few people and borrow different ideas from each. Next, spent a few minutes relaxing, using any of the techniques in **WAY 2: Switch off the stress response**, page 22, **WAY 3: Take a mindful approach to relaxation,** page 26, and **WAY 4: Practise the art of visualisation**, page 28.

Begin to visualise yourself in a situation you have coming up where you need extra confidence, with the attributes you have listed. Notice how you are looking, moving and talking. Spend time seeing yourself with these attributes, see how others are reacting to you positively too, just as you would to that confident person you first imagined. Practise this process as often as you can before the event arises, then again just before the event, then go for it!

You can almost think of it as a bit of play acting, trying out new things to see what feels right.

WAY 33

Just say 'No'

Learning this skill and using it will protect your self-esteem.

Research shows that happy people know how to set their boundaries. One workplace study in 2001 even showed that being assertive and 'disagreeable' is linked to earning more money! (22) Trying to please all the people all of the time has a negative pay-off – you lose out. If you are a caring and considerate person, you can easily fall in the trap of saying 'Yes' to everyone and everything, just because you don't want to seem 'bad' or 'selfish'.

The problem with this scenario is that sooner or later your self-esteem plummets! Think about it: if you are always putting others' needs before your own, the message you are giving to yourself is something like, 'I am bottom of the pile, everyone else comes before me, I don't matter.'

Of course, doing something helpful or kind for another person can be rewarding and actually essential in terms of meeting our need for emotional connection with others (see **WAY 1: Bulletproof your happiness**, page 20), but it is all a case of balance.

When someone requests something of you, (whether it doesn't seem essential, or you know deep down that it might actually be good for you) if your instant internal response is negative, listen to it. For example, you might get that niggling feeling in your stomach or a tightening in the chest. This is your intuition telling you this isn't going to work for you, so... just say 'No!'.

It is really important to use the word 'No', rather than skirting around it or making up 'fluffy' excuses. Avoiding the word might feel easier because it is less like a rejection. However, this is less helpful for the other person, because they are left not knowing quite where they stand. Remember that you don't have to give an excuse or convoluted explanation, you have the right to say 'No'. You might simply say, 'No, that's not possible. I appreciate you need help with this but I am just not able to help at this time', or, 'No, I'm not able to help you with that'.

SEE ALSO
- **WAY 34: Show you mean what you say and get results** (page 102)
- **WAY 35: Set your boundaries and stick to them!** (page 104)

Start off with the small stuff

The best way to start this new habit is with really small requests, so that you get practice in fairly low risk situations. Remember to use the word 'No' wherever possible, because it gives a clear message to the requester and may result in fewer attempts at persuasion. For instance, when a cold caller rings up, you could say right at the start of the call, 'No, I am not interested in talking to you about this subject. Goodbye'. You might purposefully get near a charity seller in the street, then when they approach, you can say, 'No, thank you.'

Spend some time thinking of other situations where you can practise using the word 'No', without feeling compelled to make up excuses, so that when a request comes that you really need to turn down, it will feel much easier to do so. Always remember that you are only rejecting a request, not the person making the request. You may find that people are initially a little shocked or even angry with you when you say 'No', especially if they are used to getting their own way with you! But if they are true friends, they will recover quickly and, over time, have much more respect for you. This will, in turn, increase your self-esteem!

Try this

Tip: Be aware of your body language while you are saying 'No'. By maintaining an open, friendly posture and expression, you unconsciously communicate to the other person that you are on their side and not being unreasonable. This will help them to accept the 'No'. If you are on the phone, be aware of your tone of voice, keeping it level and calm.

WAY 34

Show you mean what you say and get results

All mouth and no trousers? Recognise the importance of non-verbal communication when you want to get your point across.

When you are trying to get your point across and you notice that people just aren't listening, or you repeatedly find that people talk over you or just don't hear *what* you are saying, it might not be what you are saying, but the *way* you are saying it! 'Non-verbal communication' (ie. what you are communicating via your posture, gestures, facial expressions and tone, volume and pace of your voice) is recognised by social psychologists as extremely important. Some say that it accounts for as much as 70 per cent of the impact of your communication, leaving only 30 per cent for your words to have any influence! (23) Although this is a debatable statistic, because precise measurement is difficult, the relative importance of non-verbal communication is certainly worth paying attention to.

It is very common, when we are feeling under pressure, to get a communication 'right' in tricky circumstances, to over-focus on *what* we say, rather than *how* we deliver it.

SEE ALSO

- **WAY 32: 'Fake it till you make it'** (page 98)

Make non-verbal communication work for you

Make eye contact

About 70 per cent of the time usually feels about right. If you find this difficult, which lots of people do, practise, practise, practise, gradually increasing the proportion of time. Try it first with loved ones and those you feel comfortable around.

Keep as open a posture as possible

Unfold your arms and legs, keep your hands loose, relax your shoulders, and, ideally, have your feet flat on the ground. All of this may feel a bit unfamiliar if you are not used to it, but it is very useful for two reasons.

First, it will make you appear approachable and confident, even if you don't feel it! (see **WAY 32: 'Fake it till you make it'**, page 98). Secondly, consciously relaxing and 'opening' your body provides bio-feedback to your central nervous system that you *are* relaxed. Even if you don't feel relaxed (and you may feel very nervous if you are used to folding your arms and legs!) in time, your whole central nervous system will be in relaxation mode (see **WAY 3: Take a mindful approach to relaxation**, page 26), you will feel more grounded and centred, and so able to communicate openly.

Slow down the pace of speech and lower the tone of your voice

When nervous or feeling under pressure, most people raise both the tone and speed of their voice. This can have the effect of sounding high-pitched or squeaky, or sometimes, particularly for men, loud or 'booming'. Go against your instincts when you are trying to get your point across. Rather than rushing to get it all out, (which you might be tempted to do if you have been thinking about it for a long time), consciously slow down and lower the tone and volume of your voice. This often grabs people's attention! Remember, we are often drawn to what we are prevented from having, so making people think you are saying something special through the quality of your voice, could make them really listen! It will certainly make you appear and sound more confident and self-assured. Keep practising it and then you will feel it too! (see **WAY 32: 'Fake it till you make it'**, page 98)

Try this

WAY 35

Set your boundaries and stick to them!

Practise some assertiveness techniques that really work.

We often feel that we have to give an instant response to a request asked of us. But this is actually only a rule that we have made up for ourselves! If you are someone who struggles to draw a line, and often ends up doing things you really don't want to be doing, learning to set and stick to boundaries could really help. A well known assertiveness technique is to delay your response, so that you won't get caught off guard and agree to something you might not want to. By delaying your response, you give yourself time to think and consider:

1. Is this actually a reasonable request?

2. Is it something you are able to do without feeling over-burdened?

3. Is it something you *want* to do?

When you have considered these questions, in your own time, then you will be able to give an honest, meaningful answer, rather than agreeing on the hoof and regretting it later.

When you are asked to do something and you want to just say 'No', but feel you may struggle with that, see **WAY 33: Just say 'No',** page 100 for tips. Remember that if your gut is saying 'No', then by going against that instinct and saying 'Yes', you are chipping away at your own self-esteem. You are giving yourself the message that your needs are not important and consequently, that *you* are not important.

This is a slippery slope to feeling depressed. Being assertive means being equal to others, that is, being respectful of others *and* yourself; you both deserve that!

SEE ALSO
- **WAY 34: Show you mean what you say and get results** (page 102)
- **WAY 36: Develop rapport** (page 108)

Tip: Be armed with a phrase and give yourself space to think. Then, when someone requests something of you, which you feel in your gut might not be a good thing to agree to, simply say something like: *'I need to think about that and get back to you.'*

The person will probably want to know roughly when that might be, so if it's possible, give them a time or day when you will let them know your response. If you feel you are not able to give them a specific time, you can just say that you will let them know *'as soon as possible'*.

Be like a broken record!

The broken record technique involves repeating the same thing over and over again, just like a broken record, until you get your point across!

Here is an example:
A friend calls you and asks if you could look after her child on Thursday evening. You have planned to go an exercise class on Thursday and really want to go, as you haven't been for a while. You will see a friend there who you will have a drink with afterwards and you have been looking forward to it. So, your gut tells you, '*Say no!*'. But then guilt creeps in, you know the friend who is asking for help will have to pay a baby sitter if you don't help, and she has helped you in the past. So, you say, '*Well, I'm not sure, I'd really like to help but I might be busy. I'll have to check.*'

The friend hears that you are not definitely saying 'No', so carries on stating her case:

'*It will only be a couple of hours, I wouldn't ask unless I really had to*', and so on. You then feel under pressure and don't want to appear selfish, so before you know it, you say, '*Oh, OK, that's fine, bring her over at 6.*' The friend is very grateful. In the moment you feel the glow of being appreciated, but when the evening arrives and she rushes in, leaving you with a demanding, tired child, you feel taken advantage of, fed up and pretty worthless.

Let's look at how you could use the broken record technique to make this situation work better.

When the friend makes her request and you know, deep down, that it's just not

going to work for you, listen to that gut feeling! Then, when you have made your response of saying 'No', STICK TO IT. This means not deviating from your intention, and being like a broken record! This is the key, because if you change your response in any way, it gives the impression that there might be room for negotiation and a green light to the person to continue to try to persuade you. By repeating your original 'No' response, you are being very clear that you mean 'No'. So, in this example, you might say:

'*No, I'm afraid that's not possible for me this Thursday, but I would like to help another time.*'

If the friend then continues to try and persuade you by saying, '*But I really do need your help this Thursday*', you say *again*:

'*No, it's not possible for me this Thursday but I would like to help another time.*'

If she continues with other tactics, you just keep repeating your statement. You can always repeat back what's she's said so she feels heard, but *do not* deviate from your original statement:

'*I know you'd really like help this Thursday, but it's just not possible for me I'm afraid.*'

This may feel strange at first, but at times when you need to hold your ground, it really works. Try it!

1 2 3 4 5 6 7 8
9 10 11 12 13 14
15 16 17 18 19
20 21 22 23 24
25 26 27 28 29
30 31 32 33 34
35 **36 37 38 39
40** 41 42 43 44
45 46 47 48 49

Chapter 8

IMPROVE COMMUNICATION AND RELATIONSHIPS

Relationships are at the heart of so much of what we do in all areas of our life – work, family and leisure. This chapter will help you to hone your skills of communication and relationship building. It begins by introducing theoretical and practical techniques for developing rapport with other people, so that you can better understand how they feel and learn how to see their point of view. You can then look at some of the basic differences in the way in which men and women's brains function, which can make a big, positive difference when trying to negotiate with the opposite sex! You can learn some effective ways for diffusing conflict in relationships, helping you to express feelings and move forward, rather than get locked into destructive patterns or arguments. Finally, you can be on the look-out for relationship busters – the behaviours which may lead to conflict and melt-down. All of these approaches apply not only in intimate relationships but all relationships, with wider family members, colleagues and friends. By applying some of the ideas in practice, you can quickly feel freed and on the road to more constructive and helpful relationships in your life.

WAY 36 Develop rapport

Cultivate a good relationship by conveying that you really understand the other person.

We communicate our thoughts and feelings in both verbal and non-verbal ways. We send out signals through our posture, facial expressions, gestures, and tone and pace of voice, all of which are registered at an unconscious level by the person 'on the receiving end'. In fact, much of what we convey to others happens via what we are doing, rather than what we are saying. Understanding and using verbal and non-verbal signals to show that we understand another person is known as establishing *rapport*. It can make a big difference to the outcomes of our encounters with others, whether we are negotiating a deal, listening to our children or developing a new, intimate relationship.

Have you ever noticed the way in which two people interact by mirroring and matching each other's movements? One may cross their legs or lean to one side, and the other follows, or they may use similar facial expressions or the same metaphors to describe their experiences. This process is an in-built survival mechanism, beginning when a baby watches her mother's face and learns to smile in response to her smile, thus strengthening the bond between them. Rapport involves a 'dance' of matching movements, and the greater the match, the more likely it is that those two people will like each other and get along.

When we consciously begin to cultivate rapport with another, we aim to 'come alongside them', showing that we understand their way of seeing things. We do this by *pacing* the other person, a concept developed and utilised within NLP. Imagine if you were walking with someone. If you walk too fast, they have to try to keep up. If you walk too slowly, they have to slow down. Either way, they need to make a special effort. However, if we walk at their pace so that they are comfortable, we begin to build a sense of safety and trust. Pacing and building rapport can be done in a number of ways (24):

We can pace and match our own non-verbal behaviour to the person's:

Body language
- posture
- gestures
- eye contact
- breathing pattern

Voice
- tone, volume, speed, pitch
- pauses and sounds, eg. sighing

Language
- using the person's key words and phrases to show how we have heard and understand what they have said.

Using someone's mode of expression
We can learn to spot which mode another person primarily expresses themselves in:
- **visual**, where someone tends to say how they *see* things or picture things
- **auditory**, where someone talks about what things *sound* like to them
- **kinaesthetic**, where the person talks about how things *feel* to them.

We can use this same mode in the way that we reflect back what the person is saying, or ask them questions. For example, we can respond to a 'visual' person by saying, 'Yes, I see what you're saying' or ask a 'kinaesthetic' person what they feel about something.

Wider aspects

We can build trust and respect by reflecting someone's overall mood, showing that we understand their opinions and beliefs, sharing in their interests, and even dressing in ways which 'fit' with others we are interacting with.

Rapport is one of the main persuasive arts of the successful salesperson, but can be a powerful and positive means of enabling someone to feel listened to and understood.

Pacing practice

We all use rapport in everyday life to some extent, but here is a chance to develop your skills more consciously.

Begin with something easy. Practise pacing the rate at which someone speaks on the telephone, as you only have their auditory cues to concentrate on. When you feel practised at this, add in matching tone of voice.

Extend this practice to friends or family. Then add in body posture or mood. Practise each one systematically until you can do it without thinking. Notice the way the other person responds to you.

Try this

Tip: We need to use skill and respect when we match someone's behaviour, as exact mirroring can be too obvious. However, joining in the other person's 'dance' of movements and expressions in approximate ways can really help to give the right signals. For example, if someone is tapping their foot, we might gently tap our fingers to the same rhythm on the arm of our chair. However, avoid pacing speech problems or physical disabilities.

WAY 37

See the other person's point of view

Use a simple model for understanding others and develop a broader, detached perspective.

In any relationship and situation, there will be differing perspectives and more importantly, no 'right' perspective. In order to develop our understanding of anything more fully, we need to examine it from all angles, and this is as relevant to relationships as it is to appreciating a piece of furniture.

A simple but powerful model for building this understanding has come from the world of NLP. This involves developing three perspectives (25).

First position is your own view of the situation, ie. your own reality. It is important that you know yourself and your own values in order to be a good role model or to influence others.

Second position is where you use your imagination to understand another person's perspective (without necessarily agreeing with it). This is at the heart of empathy. You can understand their feelings, which means that you may not wish to hurt them because you can 'feel' their pain. You can also strive to understand how they think,

including the sorts of ideas and opinions they have, and how they are thinking about a specific situation.

Third position is a particularly resourceful position, because it involves stepping out of both your own standpoint and that of the other person, to a place of detached perspective. You can now see the relationship or situation from both viewpoints, and can evaluate it in the round. You can check the appropriateness of your own position, and look at the outcomes you want in a more emotionally detached and informed way.

All three positions are useful to increasing understanding, whether in a friendship or business negotiation, and particularly where there are conflicting views. In a complex situation, there may be several viewpoints and perspectives to consider.

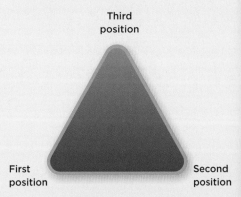

Prepare for an effective meeting

Use this exercise to prepare for a meeting involving another person, for example, a work session with your manager or discussion with the head teacher at your child's school. This should be something where you wish to develop a greater understanding, but which doesn't necessarily involve conflict or bad feelings.

Position two chairs for first and second position, as indicated in the diagram opposite.

1. Sit on your first position chair and ask yourself the following questions:
- What outcome/s do you want for the meeting?
- How will you know when you have achieved this outcome? (This is a cue to what you need to pay attention to.)
- What kind of manner are you going to adopt for the meeting?
- What is your fallback position? (Think of what you might be prepared to accept as a step forward, if the whole outcome does not seem possible. You may want to base this on maintaining a good relationship.)

2. Now, stand up, give yourself a shake and mentally leave your first position. Sit on the second position chair and think of yourself as the other person. Repeat these questions and answer them as best you can for that person. If you need to, refer to yourself by your name in order to be clear about the separation.

3. Now, stand up and 'shake off' being the other person. Move into the third position a few feet away, as indicated in the diagram above. Stand looking at the two chairs and think what is likely to happen between the two imaginary people sitting in them. Maintaining a detached and objective stance, ask questions to explore the situation, for example:
- What advice would you offer the 'you' in the chair, and what else would you like to say?
- What advice would you offer the other person?
- Are both likely to get the outcome they want, and if not, what needs to change?

4. Finally, 'shake off' the third person and go back to the first position. In the light of the information you have gained from the second and third positions, go back through the first set of questions, and see what you need to change. For example, you may see a need to change the outcome you want, or your style, or the structure of the meeting. Check these changes by going into second and third positions again, and seeing how it looks from these perspectives.

Try this

38 Strengthen the glue of relationships

Understanding vital differences between the needs of men and women can help to make sense of communication in relationships.

Deborah Tannen, a psychologist who has written prolifically about what makes relationships work in heterosexual couples (27), emphasises the importance of both partners understanding that although men and women have the same basic emotional needs, *different* needs are important and significant for men and women. This can be a huge source of discontent and disagreement in heterosexual couples (and same-sex couples where one partner is more 'male-' or 'female-brained'). Understanding what these differences are can be extremely useful in making sense of communications, particularly ones which you may have previously misunderstood and worse, interpreted as personal criticism or dismissiveness by your partner.

Remember that first and foremost, all the emotional needs listed on page 21 are essential to all human beings. Supporting each other (to the best of your ability) so that you can both get these needs met will be significant in building a happy relationship. Of course, this can mean making compromises and perhaps giving your partner space to do things that do not directly benefit you, for instance, respecting your partner's need for time alone, or take a weekend away with friends when you would prefer to be with them. Sometimes this can feel tough and ignite basic emotions of abandonment and even rejection.

However, in order to build a happy, healthy relationship, it is essential to be mindful of the need for mutual respect and allowing each other to get your needs met as *individuals*, as well as a couple.

Typically, men place greater importance on two needs: *independence* and *status*. Typically, women place greater importance on two different needs: *emotional connection* and *empathy*.

In some ways these two sets of needs are in direct conflict with each other, and this can be a great source of tension in relationships. It is important to remember that these needs are hardwired into us for our survival, so that we are emotionally driven to get these needs met. When they are not met, we can be left feeling depleted and stressed.

Tannen describes a typical situation which could occur between a heterosexual couple, which demonstrates how these needs can collide. At the beginning of an exciting and passionate relationship, the man in a couple asks the woman if she would like to stay over

> Tip: Just being aware of these differing needs can be extremely helpful in understanding why your partner may be behaving in a certain way. Next time you wind up feeling annoyed or rejected, have a look at what need might be driving your partner's behaviour. Does it differ from your own?

Negotiation is the key

Try this

If you know your partner is going to want to do something which meets their needs but not yours, discuss how you can both get your needs met. So, in the breakfast example, maybe the woman could have said, *'I know you want to read the paper and I would like to talk with you as well, so perhaps we can both read for 15 minutes, then talk for 15 minutes after that?'*

and have breakfast with him in the morning. The woman is delighted at the idea and imagines a wonderful night together, followed by a romantic breakfast, where they stare lovingly into each other's eyes and make plans for their next meeting. In reality, after a great night, the man wakes up the woman with a kiss and calls her to the breakfast table. She sits down excitedly and looks up to see him transfixed by his newspaper, where he stays for the remainder of breakfast. The woman attempts to generate conversation but his minimal responses indicate to her that he is simply not interested. She leaves after breakfast feeling devastated that the relationship is not what she thought, feeling used and let down.

The reality for him is that he likes to read his newspaper every morning over breakfast. He loves having her there with him, and being able to look up and see her smile feels really good. He is totally confused when he calls her later that day and gets a very frosty reception!

The woman's need to talk and exchange feelings and plans (*emotional connection*) was totally scuppered by the man's need to maintain his independent routine of reading the paper and catching up on news, which gives him the sense of being informed (*independence* and *status*).

39

Transform your relationship with brain science

Let go of blame and get on with each other better.

In any heterosexual relationship, whether couples, friends or colleagues, understanding some basic differences between the functioning of male and female brains can transform your communication with each other and enhance your relationship.

Men and women's brains are wired differently: fact!

A major cause of relationship breakdown is assuming that your partner thinks *the same way as you do*. How many times do you catch yourself thinking 'How could she not *see* that? How could he *forget* that? He never *listens* to me? Therefore... he/she *doesn't love/ respect me!'*

Our brains are designed to support our traditional roles in society. For men, this typically means that the corpus callosum*, the tract which connects the two brain hemispheres, is very thick with only a few substantial neural fibres. This enables men to fully focus on the task in hand, meaning that they were traditionally excellent hunters and gatherers, quick to zone in on prey in order to provide for the family.

Traditionally, women were the home-makers – bringing up children, tending to the house and fire, preparing the food which the men brought home, and networking with other women to create safe environments for their families. They evolved a corpus callosum which is multi-tracked, enabling them to attend to a number of tasks at one time.

Although the roles of men and women have changed to some degree through the centuries, with role reversal being a common concept in contemporary times, the ways in which our brains function has stayed the same.

An essential understanding for women is this: when a man is focused on one task, for example, reading the newspaper, watching TV, or thinking about work, he *cannot hear you*! It is not that he is ignoring you on purpose, rather that his brain is designed to be switched fully into that one task. You are background noise that he is not tuned into, and so he is not able to hear the content of what you are saying. Understanding that his lack of attention is not personal to you, but simply down to a difference in male/female brain functioning, can really help to take the 'blame' out of situations.

> **Tip: If you really want to get a man's attention, touch him on the arm, or ask him when would be a good time to talk, or just call him by his name and ask him to listen! However, you do it, make sure he is looking at you so that you know his attention has switched.**

One other major difference that causes problems for heterosexual couples is that men have a mode of operating that women rarely experience, called 'No Brain' (28). This mode is important for men, because their capacity for intensely focusing needs to be balanced with some 'down time' afterwards to recuperate. Think of the scenario where a woman sees a man looking glazed and asks, 'What are you thinking?' and is met with the answer, 'Nothing!' This can be incomprehensible to a woman, whose mind is typically juggling several subjects. She may be tempted to assume this cannot be possible, and that he is either hiding something or withholding intimacy, which in turn, can create tension and distance in the relationship. Understanding that men's brains must go into that void, in order to redirect themselves and bring full focus to the next task, means that a woman can relax when they see the blank expression on a man's face. He is just recharging!

Step off the circular argument

When you are feeling annoyed with each other:

Stop (Try 7/11 breathing to re-engage your thinking brain – see page 24)

Think about your partner's behaviour as being subject to the wiring of their brain! Remember, if you are the opposite sex to your partner/friend/colleague, you are wired differently, thanks to evolution.

Take time out Trying to resolve things when you are feeling emotionally heated will get you nowhere fast. Take a few minutes to breathe deeply or go for a walk to calm down before attempting to communicate.

Express your feelings without blame
If we feel attacked, as we do when 'blame language' is used, we go into survival, 'shut down' mode where we are unable to think clearly or see things in perspective. Instead, try to be specific and use the following communication rule to convey your unhappiness about what the other is doing:

'I feel … (your feeling) when you …' (their behaviour)

Be as specific as you can. Then, really listen to the other's response and together discuss practical steps forward.

Try this

SEE ALSO
- **WAY 11: SOS strategies** (page 44)
- **WAY 34: Say what you mean and get results** (page 102)
- **WAY 36: Develop rapport** (page 108)
- **WAY 37: See the other person's point of view** (page 110)

40

Beware relationship busters!

Learn ways to prevent the 'Four Horsemen of the Apocalypse' from riding into town.

Relationships matter. We know that having a supportive and loving partner boosts our mental and physical health and helps to prevent illness. The psychologist John Gottman has spent many years studying successful and unsuccessful marriages and has identified four key indicators which predispose relationships to breakdown (29). These he terms the *Four Horsemen of the Apocalypse* because their appearance signals potential relationship meltdown.

1. **Criticism** involves a 'global' attack on the person's core character, rather than just complaining about their behaviour, often with the intention of the perpetrator looking 'right' and the other looking 'wrong'. Example: *'You're a useless, lazy, waste of space!'* rather than, *'I'm cross because you didn't do the vacuuming.'* Generalisations are often used, such as, *'You're always...'*, *'You never...'*

2. **Defensiveness** comes from seeing oneself as the victim, so that the aim is to protect oneself from possible attack, even when the partner is not being critical. Behaviours include making excuses, disagreeing and countering complaints with complaints of one's own, denying responsibility, and ignoring what the partner has said.

3. **Contempt** involves insulting the person's sense of self by name-calling, swearing, using cruel or disrespectful humour and facial expressions, such as rolling the eyes and sneering.

4. **Stonewalling** involves withdrawing from the relationship as a way of avoiding conflict. Behaviours include 'the silent treatment', monosyllabic responses, changing the subject, and other responses which signify coldness or aloofness. It can involve physically removing oneself, which may be more common in men than women, and can pull individuals out of the relationship, so that they start to lead parallel lives.

Any one of the above, if used repeatedly so that it becomes an ongoing feature of behaviour in the relationship, can lead to relationship breakdown.

Gottman makes the point that it is not conflict *itself* that is the problem, but *how we handle it*. Venting feelings constructively can help to clear the air and restore balance in a relationship. However, it is important to banish the use of the 'Four Horsemen' riders by taking responsibility for the relationship, including:

- listening and validating each other's needs and wishes
- being specific about complaints and requests, rather than criticising
- using conciliatory gestures, rather than being defensive or withdrawing
- showing appreciation of each other and learning to see things from the other's viewpoint (see **WAY 37: See the other person's point of view**, page 110).

Getting professional advice can help couples to notice where things are going wrong and start to change well-practised, unhelpful behaviours.

Remember the good times

Enhance positive feelings towards your partner and notice the effect on your interaction, by trying the following activity. When you are relaxing, cast your mind back to what initially attracted you to your partner and to those early 'honeymoon' days. Remember how it felt to be together and enjoy those feelings now.

When you are with your partner, reminisce about good times, especially times when you have laughed together.

Remember something you used to enjoy together and arrange to do it now.

Try this

SEE ALSO

- **WAY 36: Develop rapport** (page 108)
- **WAY 37: See the other person's point of view** (page 110)
- **WAY 38: Strengthen the glue of relationships** (page 112)
- **WAY 39: Transform your relationship with brain science** (page 114)
- **WAY 47: Feel good about the past** (page 136)

Tip: Boost your appreciation of your partner by making a note of five, small positive things s/he does in a day. Feed these back to them at the end of the day.

1 2 3 4 5 6 7 8
9 10 11 12 13 14
15 16 17 18 19
20 21 22 23 24
25 26 27 28 29
30 31 32 33 34
35 36 37 38 39
40 **41 42 43 44**
45 46 47 48 49

Chapter 9

CHANGE UNHELPFUL PATTERNS

When we are depleted, through excessive stress, traumatic events, loneliness or boredom, we all have the potential to reach out for destructive 'quick fixes'. The common ground with any habits is that they give an initial rush of chemical-induced pleasure within the brain. However, these positive feelings are shortly followed by feelings of regret, self-loathing and a dramatic drop in mood. We are all drawn to different habits; some of us will be drawn to an instant chemical hit from alcohol, caffeine, drugs or food; some of us will use the comfort or even pain of repetitive nail-biting or skin-picking/cutting to induce the soothing hit of natural endorphins; some of us may behave in ways that temporarily get our emotional need for attention or love met, such as shopping beyond our means or sex with strangers. This chapter is focused on helping you 'take the high road' away from behaviours that you know are not working for you, however alluring they seem at the time. It introduces a cycle of change which helps you to understand how to change and how to avoid the danger of self-sabotage. You will be able to identify your 'point of no return' in habitual behaviours and then move away from it. Finally, you can learn how to develop a more compassionate approach to your habit, which avoids the emotions of shame, blame and self-criticism which in themselves can be overwhelming. These models and techniques will help you to finally leave old habits behind and develop healthy and productive ways of coping with whatever life throws your way.

WAY 41 Get out of that rut

Understand brain science and use it to grow and change.

The way the brain has evolved over millions of years is a mind-boggling process. As a species, it has taken us from monkeys to intelligent beings, able to juggle huge amounts of information and function in an increasingly complicated economic, political and social world.

There are certain mechanisms within the brain that drive this process, enabling us to grow physically, emotionally and intellectually, and giving us the incentive to keep growing, to try new things and to keep 'upping our game'. When we use our brains in this evolutionary way, this mechanism works perfectly for us, enabling us to live life to the full and to fulfil our human needs (see **WAY 1: Bulletproof your happiness**, page 20).

However, when we are overwhelmed with stress this mechanism can work against us, leading us into addictive patterns of behaviour, when we begin to rely more and more on 'chemical hits' within the brain to feel OK.

This potentially addictive process involves dopamine*, which is a chemical that is released into our blood stream in order to get us to take action.

An example of this process working well, would be as follows:

You take up canoeing. The first week, you really struggle co-ordinating everything you need to, you fall out several times and feel a bit stupid, but there is a friendly bunch of people around and you have fun. During the week, you start to feel excited about the next week's lessons, you expect to enjoy them and you look forward to it. The next week comes and you get a bit better at the technical side of things, staying in the canoe for longer. You get a sense of achievement and start to get 'the bug' for it, increasingly looking forward to future lessons, always expecting to have fun. This process of expecting fun, having fun, getting better at something, then wanting more, is dopamine working at its best for us. Dopamine is released every time we have a positive expectation and drives us forward to complete that expectation by taking action. You can see how this enables us to evolve by getting all our emotional needs met – feeling fulfilled and realising dreams and expectations of the future.

However, when we are overwhelmed by emotion and stress and our focus is narrowed and bleak, our expectations of the future are not always positive. This is when we may look for 'instant hits' to pick us up, fill a hole or just escape from what feels too painful to look at. So, in this situation, the role of dopamine can be misused by the brain and can lead us into serious trouble.

> **Tip: Use the techniques in this chapter to get these behaviours under control and allow your intelligent brain to get back in the driving seat of life's journey!**

Be on your guard for mind tricks!

Are you aware of any destructive patterns of behaviour in your life? Be honest with yourself, are there things that take up your time and energy and draw you away from more meaningful, stretching activities?

Be on your guard: these activities are the ones that can easily get out of control if you allow your brain to trick you into thinking they will make you happy.

Try this

Here's an example of how this might happen:

Work is very stressful and your relationship is going through a difficult patch. You have always enjoyed a glass of wine with dinner but recently have started having a couple before dinner too. During the stress of the day, you start to fantasise about that first glass of wine, how cool and crisp it will be, the first hit of alcohol relaxing your muscles as you sink down in your favourite chair, with the day behind you. You are creating an expectation of how wonderful that experience will be. When you get home, you have been thinking about how lovely that first sip will be for so long you can't wait, and given what a day it has been, you feel you deserve it, so you by pass your usual cup of tea, and go straight for the wine. It is nice but doesn't quite give you the pleasure you expected, so you have another. In no time at all, you've drunk over half the bottle. You decide to cancel plans with friends as you can't drive now and you are just not in the mood. This further impacts on the difficulties you are having with your partner.

In both these situations, you build tolerance to the source of pleasure. This works well when you are pursuing a healthy pleasure that stretches you (as in the canoeing example) because it enables you to work at getting better and better, because you want more and more challenge. As you improve, you get more and more natural chemical hits from endorphins ('feel-good' hormones in your body) and feel happier and more alive. But in the wine-drinking example, the process becomes destructive. As you build up tolerance, you need more and more alcohol to get that 'hit', leading to physical health problems and a more isolated, miserable life where your emotional needs are increasingly neglected. This makes you vulnerable to depression, anxiety and other serious problems.

SEE ALSO

- **WAY42: Never give up giving up!** (page 122)
- **WAY 43: Break unwanted habits** (page 126)
- **WAY 44: Show compassion to yourself** (page 128)

42 Never give up giving up!

Understand the psychology of changing habits.

Prochaska and DiClemente originally developed a model called 'The Cycle of Change' in 1984, when they were studying how smokers were able to give up their habit (30). The cycle describes the psychological process of giving up a habit, whatever that habit might be. What is so useful to understand from this model is that breaking addictive habits is generally not a linear process. It is often a case that 'slipping up' or 'relapse' is actually part of a process of stopping completely. A recent study at Coventry University, showed that the average number of times a long-term smoker gives up is seven times! (31)

The worst enemy of breaking habits is not relapse, it is self-sabotage! The bully of addiction says something like,

> 'Oh well, you have had one cigarette/alcoholic drink/food binge/cut, and now you've failed, so you may as well do the job properly and have another'

or

> 'You've failed again, you will never kick this habit, you are not like other people so don't try to pretend you are.'

This is where the real trouble starts, not with the relapse itself.

The cycle of change shows us that relapse is completely normal and that, in fact, we learn something new every time we relapse. Have a look at the model in the diagram below.

THE CYCLE OF CHANGE MODEL

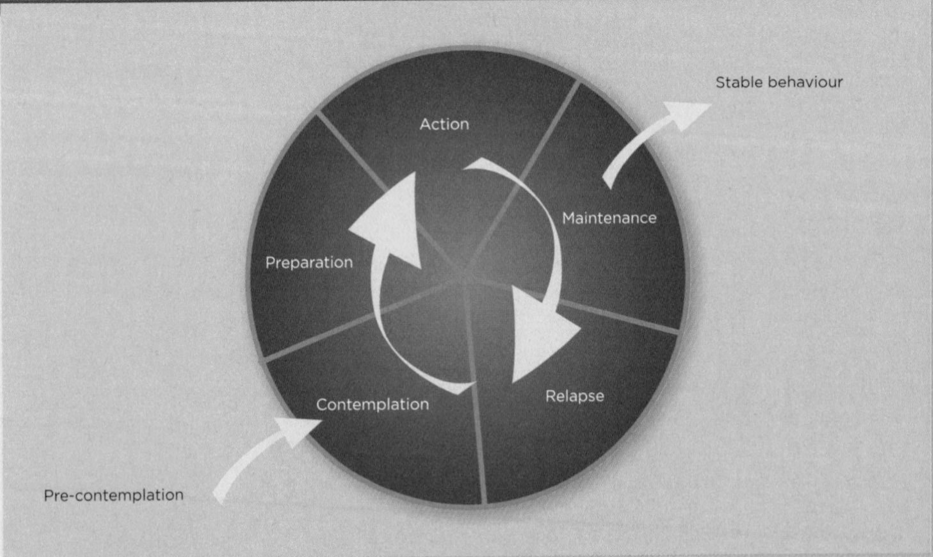

Stable behaviour

Action

Maintenance

Preparation

Relapse

Contemplation

Pre-contemplation

Pre-contemplation (not ready): Not yet acknowledging that there is a problem behaviour that needs to be changed.

Contemplation: Acknowledging that there is a problem, weighing up the pros and cons of change, but not yet ready or sure of wanting to make a change.

Action: Changing behaviour/stopping the habit.

Maintenance: Maintaining the behaviour change.

Relapse: Having a 'slip up'.

Sometimes, after a relapse we end up going around the whole cycle again. For example, we may have one cigarette and not acknowledge this to be a problem, so we have another. We are stuck in the Pre-contemplation stage, perhaps allowing the arch enemy of 'self-sabotage' to keep us there! We will need to progress around the stages of the cycle to get back in the right mindset, creating the resolve to break the habit again.

Being *aware* of this cycle can help us to regain control after a relapse more quickly, and even to bypass stages of the model, so that we can arrive back swiftly at Action and Maintenance.

SEE ALSO
• **WAY 5: What you focus on is what you get** (page 30)

Don't leave change to chance!

When you are breaking a habit, don't go about it with gritted teeth and rely on will-power alone. This will make the whole process much more painful than it actually has to be!

Make a plan, including the following steps:

1. Identify your 'high risk situations', ie. situations when you know you will be tempted to resort to the habit, such as when you are tired, or with certain people.

2. Think about which of these situations you could avoid initially. You may not need to avoid them long-term. This is just to get the ball rolling, so that you avoid putting yourself in temptation unnecessarily.

3. For the situations you do have to expose yourself to, prepare a plan of how you will deal with them. Include a relaxation strategy (see **WAY 3: Take a mindful approach to relaxation**, page 26, **WAY 4: Practise the art of visualisation**, page 28 and **WAY 8: Create an anchor for calm**, page 38) so that you can remain calm and less likely to have your intelligence 'highjacked'. Choose something you can have or do which has some reward attached to it. So, if you are giving up

smoking, you might want to take a delicious, healthy snack like a tropical fruit salad to a meeting, or promise to buy yourself something you really want when you have kicked the habit for a certain period. Include in the plan ways in which you will challenge any negative, bullying thoughts which might pop up (see **WAY 12: Tune in and tune out of negative thinking**, page 48, **WAY 13: Stand up to the bully of negative thinking**, page 50 and **WAY 14: Mind your language**, page 52). For example, if you start to think, 'I will never beat this, I want a cigarette so badly', you might switch into thinking about all the other times you have not had a cigarette when you wanted one. Use all the available evidence, for example, 'This is hard but I have resisted before and I will take it one hour at a time, I've done really well so far.'

4. Make sure you do congratulate yourself every time you resist the habit, either with words or a treat. Each time you do something different, you begin to create new templates of behaviour in your brain, meaning that doing things in the new way just gets easier and easier!

Try this

Tip: Remember, a slip up is not a disaster unless you allow it to be! Acknowledge what went wrong, take the learning from that situation and move forward, armed with more understanding of how the habit tripped you up this time.

43

Break unwanted habits

Know your point of 'no return' and then change the pattern.

It is true to say that we are creatures of habit. We lay down templates of behaviour which we believe will help to meet our emotional needs. This process is usually unintentional and unconscious, and draws on past experiences and situations where something may have worked for us. However, it can lead us into patterns or habits which turn out to be problematic, as for example, when someone with a need for intimacy develops a habit of over-eating as a means of providing a sense of internal 'comfort'.

Breaking these patterns requires that we understand how we 'do' the pattern which leads us to the 'point of no return' – the point at which we unconsciously reach for a cigarette or chocolate biscuit, or start to bite our nails or grind our teeth. At this moment, we are in a trance state, completely and narrowly focused on the expectation of pleasure which we will experience once we take this final step. By understanding the thoughts, feelings and actions which lead up to this point of no return which forces us to act, we can bring the whole pattern into full consciousness. This enables us to make a choice to divert away from this critical point towards more resourceful behaviour. The end result is that we feel better about ourselves and more in control.

> **Tip:** Ask yourself what emotional need or needs your habit is trying to address, using the list of emotional needs in **WAY 1: Bulletproof your happiness** on page 20. How can you meet these in more healthy or appropriate ways? What support will you need? Imagine how it will be to get your needs met in these better ways.

Move away from the point of no return

1. Take a sheet of paper and write down all the things you think about, feel and do which lead you to the point of no return with your habit, in the order in which they occur, up to the point of no return. This is the point where it seems that you are in an 'addictive trance' and cannot turn back, for example:

Habit: Eating a packet of biscuits in the evening
- I sit on the settee watching TV after my dinner (action)
- I feel a bit bored (feeling)
- I start to imagine the biscuits in the kitchen cupboard (thought)
- My mouth starts watering (feeling)
- I think, 'I still feel a bit hungry, I'll just have a biscuit and then I'll feel a bit fuller' (thought)
- I get up and walk into the kitchen, opening the cupboard door (action)
- I see the biscuits and start to feel even hungrier (feeling)
- I think, 'I may as well take the packet back to the living room' (thought)
- I reach for the packet (action and point of no return)

2. Having identified your point of no return, jot down some ideas of how you might divert away from it, just before you reach it, for example:

Leave the kitchen and phone my friend. If there is nothing interesting on TV, watch a DVD I enjoy.

Go for a walk or run round the block.

Sit at my computer and find out information for my holiday.

Try to think of alternatives which are enjoyable and fulfilling, and help to meet the emotional needs you have identified in healthier or better ways.

3. Now spend a few minutes relaxing, using 7/11 breathing (**WAY 2: Switch off the stress response**, page 22) or a mindfulness practice (**WAY 3: Take a mindful approach to relaxation**, page 26). Then, imagine going through the steps to just before your point of no return. At this point, float out of yourself and watch yourself in a detached way. See yourself diverting away from your point of no return into something that absorbs you. Float back into yourself and notice how this feels. What is it like to not be driven by addictive thinking or behaviour and to be doing something more beneficial?

4. Write down some of these positive thoughts and feelings. Practise your new pattern in your mind as often as you can. Notice the positive differences in the situation which result from your new behaviour.

Try this

WAY 44 Show compassion to yourself

Being kind and supportive to yourself is an empowering way to start changing your habits.

The compassionate mind approach (32) to human psychology is gaining acceptance as a way of helping us to change unhealthy ways of thinking and behaving, particularly when the prospect of change can just seem too difficult. Developing a compassionate approach to our problems, for example, our relationship with food, alcohol or smoking, avoids the emotions of shame, blame and self-criticism, which in themselves can be overwhelming.

A compassionate approach has a number of elements:

Understanding what we're up against
For example, if we are struggling with obesity, we can understand how the food industry is geared to stoking our appetites, through including 'eat more' chemicals in many foods and by promoting larger and larger portion sizes which are dense in fat, sugar and calories. We can also understand that our human brains are designed to prompt us to eat when food is available, going back to times when our ancestors needed to forage and when food was often in short supply.

Taking control and responsibility for change
While the relationship with something like food is complex, understanding the problems we face can help us to move away from self-blaming and begin to help ourselves in a more compassionate and responsible way.

Being kind and supportive towards ourselves
Knowing that over-eating is not our fault, but that we can take responsibility for it, leads on to appreciating that we can gain control over it, too, if we can be kind and supportive to ourselves along the way. Kindness is not about treating ourselves to a big ice cream when we have managed to eat less for a week, but rather ensuring that we are meeting our real emotional needs, and this is a foundation stone to well-being (see **WAY 1: Bulletproof your happiness**, page 20).

We have already seen how important it is to switch off our stress response (Chapter 2) and control our negative thinking (Chapter 3) in order to avoid intense emotions such as anxiety, anger and shame. However, there are areas of the brain, and particular hormones, which respond to self-compassion and to the kindness of others, and which can help to defuse any sense of threat.

Compassion plays a key role in being able to develop happiness within ourselves and in our relationships with others, generating more resourceful thoughts, emotions and actions which we can bring to bear on changing our habits. At the heart of developing compassion is the desire to relieve our own and others' suffering. To develop compassionate motives, we need to understand our values and the kind of person that we want to be.

So how can we develop a compassionate mind? Try the following activity which provides a significant first step.

Visualise the compassionate self

It is difficult to offer ourselves compassion if we do not know what it feels like. It takes practice!

Give yourself some time to relax in a quiet place. Spend a few minutes breathing from the belly and allowing the body to slow down a little. If you need more time, follow one of the relaxation activities in **WAY 3: Take a mindful approach to relaxation**, page 26 and **WAY 4: Practise the art of visualisation**, page 28.

Think of all the qualities you would like to have as a compassionate person, for example, wisdom, responsibility, kindness, warmth.

Take each quality in turn and imagine being a person who thinks, feels and acts with this quality. For example, imagine being a warm person. How does your body respond, for example, your posture, facial expression, inner sensations? Imagine yourself as that warm person interacting with others – how you speak, what you say, how you move in relation to them. For example, you might hear the warmth in the tone of your voice, or how you express warmth in non-verbal ways towards someone who is suffering. Once you have experienced each quality in action, imagine bringing them all together into that compassionate person you are. What would that be like for yourself and others? Imagine letting go of any emotions of self-blame and taking responsibility for change.

When you are ready, bring yourself back to full wakefulness.

NOTE
If you find this difficult, imagine creating a compassionate friend in the same way.

Try this

Tip: Encourage yourself to take actions which are in your best interests, and the interests of others. Start with very small steps which are easy to do, and prepare yourself for practising new skills you may need. Give yourself encouraging and kind thoughts along the way.

1 2 3 4 5 6 7 8
9 10 11 12 13 14
15 16 17 18 19
20 21 22 23 24
25 26 27 28 29
30 31 32 33 34
35 36 37 38 39
40 41 42 43 44
45 46 47 48 49

Chapter 10

REACH THE PEAK OF WELL-BEING

This final chapter helps you to put the icing onto the cake of well-being. Having explored how to use the mind to recover and improve well-being in a number of key ways, you can turn your attention to what you want and how you wish to feel as you move forwards in your life. You can use the power of the 'dreaming brain' to come up with new ideas and solutions. Much of this chapter is based on positive emotions as the key to building resilience and a lifetime of well-being. This includes how to develop positive emotions about the future, through cultivating optimism; positive emotions about the past, through gratitude and forgiveness; and positive emotions about the present, through using your signature strengths and enjoying the benefits of getting into flow. Finally, we all have the opportunity of connecting our 'inner spirit' with our outer world, in terms of discovering a meaning and purpose in life. Paying attention to this need for connection can enhance our mental and physical health and completes the 'circle' of well-being. It enables us to give out and connect with others, to appreciate the beauty in the world and continue to be curious about our well-being and our very existence.

WAY 45

Daydream your way into problem-solving

Use the power of the dreaming brain to go in search of solutions.

While the left side of the brain handles logic, lists, words, numbers and rational analysis, the right side is concerned with very different activities: daydreaming, imagination, images, rhythm, colour, music and spatial awareness. Einstein once said that 'imagination is more important than knowledge'. Like many other great scientists, he would deliberately spend time 'daydreaming' to engage the powers of the creative side of the brain. Einstein was not at his desk or working on a blackboard when he came up with the theory of relativity; he was relaxing on a hillside in the sunshine, imagining sitting on a sunbeam!

When we engage the immense resource of our imagination, we often experience a feeling that time is standing still. Our thoughts slow down, awareness of activity and noise around us fades out and we seem to reach a quiet, inner space full of potential. From this place, we can generate new ways of seeing things and a wider range of possible solutions. In fact, when we are wrestling with a problem, it is a good idea to allow ourselves a break from analysing it with the conscious mind, and allow the unconscious mind to go in search of ideas. We may then experience solutions popping up, seemingly out of nowhere, and at times when the problem seems to be far from our consciousness.

You can access the REM state when not fully asleep by daydreaming, which involves taking your mental focus on an inward journey. This is a natural state we dip into at various times of the day when we find our mind 'wandering' or 'drifting off', for example, when we look up from our work to look out of the window and become completely absorbed in watching the clouds. Set aside a time to deliberately daydream your way into problem-solving, using the following activity.

SEE ALSO

- **WAY 4: Practise the art of visualisation** (page 28)
- **WAY 26: Dream yourself into sleep** (page 82)

Tip: Sleeping is a time when we regularly engage the 'dreaming brain', known as REM (rapid eye movement) state. When you go to bed at night, keep a notebook by your side, so that you are ready to jot down any ideas which arise on wakening.

Generate a creative flow

You will need a piece of paper and a pencil or coloured pens.

Begin by relaxing for a few minutes, perhaps by using a mindfulness meditation (see **WAY 3: Take a mindful approach to relaxation**, page 26).

Then spend some time just drifting on a fantasy voyage, for example, imagining you are swimming under the sea, floating in a balloon or driving on an open road in an inspiring, safe space. Examine what is there from different perspectives, using all your senses: looking with interest; hearing sounds; touching and feeling textures.

Notice all the details in the scene, like a curious observer, for example, varieties of flowers or shapes of clouds or sounds of birdsong. Cycle through different sights, sounds and feelings in your mind several times until you begin to dream a little. This will help to prepare you to see things in a new and different way.

When you are ready, bring yourself gently into full consciousness and continue to go about your day without focusing on your problem. Be ready to catch any ideas which pop up unexpectedly.

Try this

WAY 46 Cultivate optimism

Use positive psychology to see the possibilities in life and put your signature strengths into action.

Martin Seligman's work over the past two decades has charted a new approach to living with 'flexible optimism' and has stimulated the growth of 'positive psychology', which focuses on strengths rather than weaknesses. He shows how developing positive emotion in our lives can lead to better relationships, improved physical health, longer lives and greater achievement (33). In fact, one of the best predictors of successful aging is joy in living (34).

Cultivating optimism and positive emotions leads to thinking about life's events in a more positive and hopeful light. Bad events are seen as being caused by external factors, specific to one area of life and likely to pass. The optimist is able to take comfort from their perceived strengths and other parts of their life where things are going well. When good events happen, they interpret them as a result of their own traits and abilities, that is, from more permanent causes than just good luck. Perceived success makes them try even harder, and they 'get on a roll', feeling the benefits across all areas of their lives. This outlook contrasts with the pessimistic thinking associated with depression, which we saw in **WAY 15: Beat the blues**, page 54. Staying hopeful is more than looking at the world through rose-tinted glasses. It is believing that they have both the will and the way that gives the optimist the resilience to cope with challenge and adversity.

Seligman argues that optimism can be learned. A key skill is learning to reframe your experiences in a more hopeful light. As we saw in the chapter on negative thinking (Chapter 3), an important factor in determining our happiness is not just what happens to us, but how we 'frame' or give meaning to our experience. Learning to relax and engage the observing self gives us a chance to break out of disempowering ways of perceiving our reality – including our problems. We begin to see that there are alternative and more hopeful ways of seeing our situation, which open up possibilities, rather than closing them down. It is like throwing open the shutters on a window and getting a wider, more inspiring view.

SEE ALSO
- **WAY 13: Stand up to the bully of negative thinking** (page 50)

> **Tip:** We all know that feeling happy makes you smile, but did you know that putting a smile on your face makes you feel happier? James Laird's research has shown that acting happy (or indeed, acting as if you are feeling any emotion), prompts us to feel that emotion (35). So make your smile as wide as possible, lifting your eyebrow muscles upwards and holding your happy expression for about 20 seconds.

Positive emotions come from using our personal strengths, giving us a sense of gratification and helping to make our lives more authentic. While eating a cream cake may give us momentary pleasure, showing kindness by helping someone in need provides a longer lasting sense of gratification. Strengths such as kindness, courage and integrity are enduring traits which can be built through teaching, practice and persistence.

Unlike talents, which are we either have or do not have, we can choose to build our strengths and can feel elevated and inspired when we use them. Owning and choosing to use our strengths is at the heart of positive psychology. In contrast, many psychological interventions place individuals in a more passive role, by focusing on repairing the damage which might have been done to them via external events.

Identify your signature strengths (and then use them)

Martin Seligman identified 24 strengths which are valued in almost every culture of the world. Register on the Authentic Happiness website and take the Brief Strengths test, based on these 24 strengths.

See: **http://www.authentichappiness.sas. upenn.edu**

Alternatively, write down three character strengths which you feel you actively employ in your life, and three more which you seldom use. These may be hard for you to identify or recognise. It may help for you to think about the major challenges you have faced in life and which strengths you used to get you through. Alternatively, you could ask the people closest to you what strengths they recognise in you.

Which are your top three strengths? Be aware of these as you go through your day-to-day life and find even more opportunities to use them.

Every day for the next seven days, use a top signature strength in a new way, for example, in a new setting or with a new person.

Choose a strength where you did not score very highly or which you have identified as one you seldom employ. How might you practise and develop this strength? Use **WAY 28: Set realistic goals**, page 88 and **WAY 29: Keep goals SMART**, page 90, to set some specific, achievable goals.

Try this

47 Feel good about the past

Developing positive emotions about the past and letting go of the bad stuff can boost your physical and emotional well-being.

Our feelings about the past can range widely across emotions of contentment and fulfilment to bitterness, anger and injustice. These emotions are determined by our thoughts about the past. Aaron T. Beck, an American psychiatrist who pioneered cognitive behaviour therapy (CBT) in the 1960s, demonstrated how thoughts influence feelings and behaviour. Certainly, it is clear that the thoughts of depressed people are dominated by their negative interpretations of the past, and we have already looked at how learning to argue against these ways of thinking can be a way out of depression (see **WAY 13: Stand up to the bully of negative thinking**, page 50, **WAY 15: Beat the blues**, page 54 and **WAY 16: Avoid the depression cycle**, page 56).

Our memories, thoughts and interpretations about the past can lock us into negative feelings which have a detrimental impact on our health and well-being. So how can we bring positive emotions about the past into our present?

We can:
- cultivate a sense of gratitude which helps us to savour and appreciate the good things that have happened in our lives
- forgive as a way of freeing ourselves from the power of past events and the intense negative emotions which may be attached to them

- focus on what went right for us in the past, including our successes, rather than what went wrong.

Even though we cannot forget bad events, forgiving removes the emotional 'sting' which blocks our capacity to experience contentment in the present. We often hold back from forgiving because of our sense of justice, as if forgiving takes away the right and proper need for revenge or for punishment of the transgressor. However, the only person we are punishing is ourselves, because our ongoing anger and bitterness diminishes our enjoyment of the present. Below is a five-stage process for forgiving called REACH, developed by the psychologist Everett Worthington and shown to have sizeable effects on reducing negative emotions and improving reported health (36):

R – Recall the hurt in as objective a way as possible.
E – Empathise, or try to understand from the perpetrator's point of view why this person hurt you.
A – Give an **altruistic** gift of forgiveness, first recalling a time when you were forgiven.
C – Commit yourself to forgive publicly, for example, by writing a letter to the perpetrator, writing it in a diary, or telling a trusted friend what you have done
H – Hold onto forgiveness by distracting away from the memories (see **WAY 11: SOS strategies**, page 44) and reminding yourself that you have forgiven.

NOTE
Some of these steps are challenging and it is important to seek professional support if you are experiencing intense emotion around particular memories.

Focus on how far you have come

Set aside some time for quiet reflection. Remember a particular time when you demonstrated positive qualities like kindness and forgiveness, and when you felt content and fulfilled. You may wish to write your thoughts and feelings down in a journal or express them in a poem or picture. Feel the gratitude which this simple exercise evokes – gratitude for being you, appreciation of others, and past enjoyment of events and surroundings.

You may wish to extend this exercise by imagining what it would be like to forgive someone for a past wrong-doing. How and in what way could you express your forgiveness?

How might it feel to let go of any negative feelings and thoughts about the person? When you are ready, notice how you feel now.

Try this

Tip: When you get into bed at night, spend a few moments remembering three reasons to be grateful for the day which has just ended.

WAY 48 Get into flow

Getting into a state of flow can optimise positive experience and achievement.

Have you ever become so absorbed in a pleasurable activity – reading, writing, gardening, painting, woodwork, sailing – only to realise later that two or more hours have passed in no time at all? It is not that your attention has wandered, but that you have been so focused, that time has disappeared and, along with it, any sense of your surroundings. You will probably have felt positive, energised and totally aligned with the task in hand, freed from worry or anxiety. This is known as being in a state of flow* and is a rewarding, even blissful, state which many performers, whether sports people, dancers, musicians, artists or writers, utilise to make the difference between a competent and outstanding outcome.

The flow state, or being 'in the 'zone'as athletes call it, has been defined and popularised by psychologist Mihály Csíkszentmihályi (37). The necessary conditions for flow are that we are sufficiently challenged to test our skills, yet our skills are such that we can just meet the challenge. We are stretched to the limit and performing at our peak.

Csíkszentmihályi's work showed that in addition to having the necessary skills and techniques, peak performers are able to deliver consistently high levels of functioning on demand. This requires that they have an undivided focus of attention, a sense of control over what they are doing, with no emotions or worries about success or failure, and can lose the sense of self-consciousness which sometimes gets in the way of an excellent performance. It is almost as if their actions and awareness are merged, like a musician merging with her instrument. The activity becomes almost automatic and the involvement almost effortless. There is a feeling of total absorption, of being in the moment, without thinking about what needs to be done or what comes next.

How can we develop our capacity to get into 'the zone', whether in our career, public performance, sport or even just fully participating in a discussion or hobby? Here are some pointers:

* **Check out your skill level**. If you are still learning, you will need to stay more 'conscious' of your actions and won't be ready to get into flow.

* **Reduce performance anxiety** with calming practices such as mindfulness meditation or anchoring (see **WAY 3: Take a mindful approach to relaxation**, page 26 and **WAY 8: Create an anchor for calm**, page 38) which will lessen worrying and help you to re-evoke positive past experiences.

* **Trust the unconscious**, rather than try to consciously focus on each movement or action. Thoughts and judgments will break the flow, as these activate the 'analyser' part of the brain, rather than the 'integrator' part of the brain.

* **Focus on the process and the moment**, rather than on outcomes and external factors like how you look to others.

* **Believe in the possibility of the impossible**. Most people have no idea of what they are capable of doing.

Many performers mentally rehearse their peak performance repeatedly, which gives them a competitive edge. Researchers have shown that when you do this, the muscles you would normally be using show a tiny amount of stimulation (38). In this way the muscles 'remember' the practice, in the same way that your brain remembers patterns of action and timing. You benefit from the mental rehearsal just as if you had practised for real. The following activity takes this on a step further, into peak performance.

Tip: Flow occurs somewhere between the boredom of too little challenge and the anxiety of demands which are too much to handle. Identify activities where you experience a pleasurable level of challenge and absorption. Spend more time doing these and less time in low-challenge, apathy-inducing activities like watching TV.

Access peak performance

To get into flow, you need to access the difference between when your 'performance' goes well and when it doesn't go so well.

Find a couple of chairs. Sit in one chair and relax for a couple of minutes, by focusing on the belly rising and falling as your breathe in and out. Begin to access a time when you performed well and slow it right down, feeling every movement, every relevant sound or visual cue, even noticing how you breathed. There will be a moment when you were at your very best, when the performance 'surrounded' you and became you in your mind. 'Walk' into that single moment of flow and get a sense of what makes it so special, what it feels like, what components seem to be different from an ordinary performance.

Change chairs and think about a time when things didn't go so well. Get a sense of this right from before you began, then slow it down and sense any difference in your posture, thoughts, breathing and so on.

Go back to the peak performance chair and get a sense of the very first step of the process when things go well. What is the difference? Are your thoughts different? Do you know how you get yourself into this positive state?

Change chairs and get into the state of when things are not going well. Try to change it to a positive state, using what you have learned.

Now change seats one last time and leave any difficult times behind. Re-access that state when things are going well in as much detail as you can. Recollect that time when the unconscious mind 'takes over' and you can just enjoy what you are doing so well. Imagine a time ahead when you would like to access peak performance.

Go through those early steps and get a sense of making the natural shift into the flow state, rehearsing your performance in your mind.

Try this

WAY 49 Connect with the whole

Explore your inner spirit and develop a sense of connection to complete the circle of well-being.

One of our basic human needs is feeling a part of a wider community, a need to feel connected to something bigger than ourselves (see **WAY 1: Bulletproof your happiness**, page 20). Throughout this guide, we have explored the links between mental, emotional and physical well-being. However, there is a fourth, spiritual dimension of well-being, which gives meaning to our existence and fulfils our need to connect to something beyond our ego – whether it is community, nature, a universal life force or the divine. Fostering our spirituality enables us to understand where we fit into the larger scheme of things. This can provide an important source of comfort and also a guide for our actions.

In an increasingly consumerist and individualistic society, it is easy to become focused on our own needs and wants. Discovering our inner spirit and innermost values can enable us to move beyond the fear and negative thinking associated with our self-centredness, to feeling more in touch with the welfare of other individuals, our communities and our environment. We are able to extend compassion, to give outwards, and, at the same time, experience a sense of wholeness within ourselves.

Spirituality relates to our experience of being human, including the discovery of meaning and purpose in life and how we rise to the challenges life presents. It is essentially about the connection we forge between that inner 'spirit' and the world of which we are part. There is a growing body of evidence that religion and spirituality can have a positive impact on the way a patient perceives and experiences illness, and can be beneficial to both mental and physical health (39). Religion can provide some people with an important faith community, with rituals and frameworks which can help them cope with life. However, we do not need to belong to an organised religion to feel that we have important personal values and a purpose in living.

Most religions and spiritual philosophies foster positive emotions such as love and forgiveness, and Martin Seligman's work has demonstrated that happy people are more likely to demonstrate altruism (40). Gratitude is another emotion linked to well-being. Research done by Robert Emmons and Michael McCullough showed that those who kept a daily gratitude journal – writing down things for which they were grateful on a daily basis – experienced higher levels of emotional *and* physical well-being (41). Being grateful can transcend our own, narrow concerns and connect us to something positive outside ourselves, for example, the goodess of others, the beauty of nature, or the wonder of the divine. The experience of 'transcendence' can be accompanied by a sense of awe, as when we appreciate a starry sky or a glorious sunset.

In 2008 the UK's Foresight Project published its findings from taking an independent and unparalleled look at how best to foster well-being within the nation.

Connect, give, take notice

Connect with the people around you. With family, friends, colleagues and neighbours. At home, work, school or in your local community. Think of these as the cornerstones of your life and invest time in developing them. Building these connections will support and enrich you every day.

Give Do something nice for a friend, or a stranger. Thank someone. Smile. Volunteer your time. Join a community group. Look out, as well as in. Seeing yourself, and your happiness, as linked to the wider community can be incredibly rewarding and creates connections with the people around you.

Take notice Be curious. Catch sight of the beautiful. Remark on the unusual. Notice the changing seasons. Savour the moment, whether you are walking to work, eating lunch or talking to friends. Be aware of the world around you and what you are feeling. Reflecting on your experiences will help you appreciate what matters to you.

Extracts from *Foresight Mental Capital and Wellbeing Project (2008). Final Project Report – Executive summary.* London: The Government Office for Science, p22.

Try this

It considered the best available scientific and other evidence to identify the factors that influence an individual's mental development and well-being, from conception until death (42).

The project identified five suggestions for individual action in terms of promoting well-being, three of which are connected to the themes of this final piece and provide the final 'Try this' activity above.

SEE ALSO
• **WAY 47: Feel good about the past** (page 136)

Tip: Think of a time when you felt inspired, connected and fully 'you'. What personal values do you now see were in operation at the time?

REFERENCES

1. Griffin J and Tyrrell I (2004) Human Givens – *A new approach to emotional health and clear thinking*. Chalvington, UK: HG Publishing.
2. Kabat-Zinn, J (2004) *Full Catastrophe Living. How to cope with stress, pain and illness using mindfulness meditation*. London: Piatkus.
3. Ludwig D and Kabat-Zinn J (2008) Mindfulness in Medicine. *Journal of the American Medical Association* **300** (11) 1350–1352.
4. Walker Atkinson W (1908) *Thought Vibration or the Law of Attraction in the Thought World*. Chicago: The New Thought Publishing Company. Re-edited and re-published in 2008 by Seed of Life Publishing, USA.
5. Kerkhof A (2010) *Stop Worrying* (p.24). Maidenhead: Open University Press (McGraw-Hill).
6. Deikman A (1982) *The Observing Self: Mysticism and Psychotherapy*. Boston: Beacon Press.
7. Peterson C, Maier S and Seligman M (1995) *Learned Helplessness: A Theory for the Age of Personal Control*. New York: Oxford University Press.
8. Griffin J (1997) The Origin of Dreams. *The Therapist Ltd*, distributed by Chalvington UK: HG Publishing.
9. Teasdale J, Segal Z, Williams et al (2000) Prevention of relapse/recurrence in major depression by mindfulness-based cognitive therapy. *Journal of Consulting and Clinical Psychology* **68** 615–623.
10. Ma S and Teasdale J (2004) Mindfulness-based cognitive therapy for depression: Replication and exploration of differential relapse prevention effects. *Journal of Consulting and Clinical Psychology* **72** 31–40.
11. Siegel D (2012) *The Developing Mind: How relationships and the brain interact to shape who we are (2nd edition)*. New York: Guilford Press.
12. Ader R et al (1995) Psychoneuroimmunology: interactions between the nervous system and immune system. *Lancet* **345** (99).
13. Martin P (2005) *The Sickening Mind: Brain, behaviour, immunity and disease* (p54). London: Harper Perennial.
14. http://www.ibshypnosis.com/IBSresearch.html
15. O'Hanlon W and Hexum A (1991) *An Uncommon Casebook: The complete clinical work of Milton H Erickson*, MD. London: W W Norton.
16. Melzack R and Wall P (1965) Pain mechanisms: a new theory. *Science* **150** 971-9.
17. Martin P (2005) *The Sickening Mind: Brain, behaviour, immunity and disease* (p250). London: Harper Perennial.
18. Griffin J (2005) *Freedom from Addiction: The secret behind successful addiction busting*. Chalvington, UK: HG Publishing.
19. www.attitudespecialist.co.nz/self-esteem.html
20. Lovelace R (1990) *Stress Master*. Chichester, UK: John Wiley & Sons.
21. Wiseman R (2012) *Rip It Up. The radically new approach to changing your life*. London: Macmillan.
22. University of Notre Dame (2001) *Mr Nice Guy: Being genetically disagreeable gets you paid at work*. Mendoza College of Business. Available at www.medicalnewstoday.com/articles/232830.php

23. Borg J (2010) *Body Language: 7 Easy Lessons to Master the Silent Language*. FT Press.

24. O'Connor J (2001) *NLP Workbook. A practical guide to achieving the results you want*. London: Element.

25. First put forward by John Grinder and Judith DeLozier and developed from the work of Gregory Bateson. Bateson G (1972) *Steps to an Ecology of Mind*. San Francisco: Chandler Publishing.

26. Adapted from The Effective Meeting Pattern in O'Connor J (2001) *NLP Workbook. A practical guide to achieving the results you want* (pp36–37). London: Element.

27. Tannen D (1991) *You Just Don't Understand; Men and women in conversation*. New York: Ballantine Books.

28. Moir A and Jessel D (1992) *Brain Sex: The Real Difference Between Men and Women*. New York: Dell Publishing.

29. Gottman J (1994) *Why Marriages Succeed or Fail ...and How You Can Make Yours Last*. New York: Simon & Schuster.

30. Prochaska J and DiClemente C (1984) *The Transtheoretical Approach: Towards a Systematic Eclectic Framework*. Homewood, IL, USA: Dow Jones Irwin.

31. Worrall P and Cooper C (2012) *The Quality of Working Life. Managers' Wellbeing, Motivation and Productivity*. Available at http://www.mbsportal.bl.uk/taster/ subjareas/mgmt/cmi/134042qualitywl12.pdf

32. Gilbert P (2009) *The Compassionate Mind*. London: Constable Robinson.

33. Seligman M (2003) *Authentic Happiness*. London: Nicholas Brealey.

34. Vaillant G (2000) Adaptive mental mechanisms: their role in Positive Psychology. *American Psychologist* **55** 89–98.

35. Flack Jr W, Laird J and Cavallaro L (1974) Separate and combined effects of facial expressions and bodily postures on emotional feelings. *Journal of Personality and Social Psychology* **29** (4) 475–486.

36. E Worthington (Ed) (1998) *Dimensions of Forgiveness: Psychological research and theological perspectives*. Philadelphia: Templeton Foundation Press.

37. Csíkszentmihályi M (1992) *Flow: The Psychology of Happiness*. London: Riderche.

38. Jacobson E (1932) Electrophysiology of mental activities. *American Journal of Psychology* **44a**.

39. Bauer-Wu S and Farran C (2005) Meaning in life and psycho-spiritual functioning: a comparison of breast cancer survivors and healthy women. *Journal of Holistic Nursing* **23** 172–190.

40. Diener E and Seligman M (2002) Very Happy People. *Psychological Science* **13** 81–84.

41. Emmons R and McCullough M (2004) *The Psychology of Gratitude*. Oxford: Oxford University Press.

42. *Foresight Mental Capital and Wellbeing Project* (2008) London: The Government Office for Science.

GLOSSARY

Adrenaline

Adrenaline is a hormone produced by the adrenal glands during high stress or exciting situations. This powerful hormone is part of the human body's acute stress response system, also called the 'fight-or-flight' response. It works by stimulating the heart rate, contracting blood vessels, and dilating air passages, all of which work to increase blood flow to the muscles and oxygen to the lungs, preparing the body for 'action'.

Amygdala

The amygdala is an almond-shaped structure deep within the limbic brain, which is involved in the processing of emotions such as fear, anger and pleasure, and determining what memories are stored and where the memories are stored in the brain. This appears to depend on how huge an emotional response an event invokes. In the case of high emotional arousal (perceived danger), the amygdala triggers the stress ('fight-or-flight') response via the hypothalamus.

Cognitive Behavioural Therapy (CBT)

Cognitive behavioural therapy (CBT) was pioneered by Dr Aaron Beck. It is a form of psychological therapy which examines the relationship between thoughts (cognitions) and how they influence feelings and behaviours. CBT interventions are designed to help people identify negative patterns of behaviour and to develop and practise more positive and healthy ways of thinking. It is used to treat depression, anxiety, anger, chronic pain and other conditions with a significant psychological component.

Corpus callosum

The corpus callosum (Latin: tough body) is a wide, flat bundle of neural fibres which connects the left and right cerebral hemispheres and facilitates communication between them. It is the largest white matter structure in the brain, consisting of 200–250 million nerve fibre projections running from one side to the other.

Dopamine

Dopamine is a neurotransmitter that helps control the brain's reward and pleasure centres, as well as helping to regulate movement and emotional responses. It enables us not only to see rewards, but to take action to move toward them.

Fight-or-flight response (see Stress response)

Flow

Flow is the mental state in which a person in an activity is fully immersed in a feeling of energized focus, full involvement, and success in the process of the activity. Proposed by Mihály Csíkszentmihályi, the positive psychology concept has been applied within a variety of fields. In flow, the emotions are not just contained and channelled, but positive, energized, and aligned with the task at hand. In a state of depression or anxiety we are be barred from flow. The hallmark of flow is a feeling of spontaneous joy, even rapture, while performing a task, although flow can also described as a deep focus on nothing but the activity – not even oneself or one's emotions.

Human Givens

The Human Givens approach, named by Joe Griffin and Ivan Tyrell, is an organising idea, drawn from both ancient wisdom and the latest scientific understandings from neurobiology and psychology, which provides a holistic, scientific framework for understanding the way that individuals and society work. At its core is the highly empowering idea that human beings, like all organic beings, come into this world with a set of needs. If those needs are met appropriately, it is not possible to suffer from mental ill-health, including depression, psychosis, addictive or self-harming behaviour.

Hypnotherapy

Hypnotherapy utilises hypnosis as a way of helping people to change unwanted patterns of behaviour. Leading exponent of hypnosis, psychiatrist Milton H. Erickson, clearly demonstrated the clinical value of this tool, which accesses the state of consciousness in which nature programmes the brain and can re-programme it. The Ericksonian approach departed from traditional hypnosis by stressing the importance of interaction with the patient and actively engaging with their inner resources and experiential life (in contrast to issuing standardised instructions to a passive subject). In doing so, it revolutionised the practice of hypnotherapy and brought many original concepts of communication and therapeutic working into the field.

Limbic system

Sometimes known as the 'emotional brain', the limbic system is the set of brain structures that forms the inner border of the cortex and is considered to include the amygdala, which signals stimuli involving reward or fear to the cortex, and the hippocampus, which is required for the formation of long-term memories.

Metaphor

An idea which is used to suggest a likeness or analogy between one thing and another. We all use metaphors to describe our situation or condition. Used therapeutically, a metaphor such as a word, phrase or story might be offered to the client to give them a different way of seeing their problem.

Mindfulness meditation

A technique for turning off busy thoughts, derived from Buddhist meditation practices. It involves focusing awareness on moment-by-moment experience, for example focusing on the breath entering and leaving the nose.

Mindfulness-based Stress Reduction (MBSR)

A structured group programme that employs mindfulness meditation to alleviate suffering associated with physical, psychosomatic and psychiatric disorders. The programme is non-religious and is based upon a systematic procedure to develop enhanced awareness of moment-to-moment experience of perceptible mental processes. It has been shown to be effective in alleviating chronic pain, depression and anxiety disorders.

Neuro-Linguistic Programming (NLP)

Neuro-Linguistic Programming, or NLP, was first developed by Richard Bandler and John Grinder in the 1970s and is now widely applied within psychotherapy, interpersonal communications and management training. Through understanding how we structure and give meaning to our internal, subjective world, NLP enables us to learn how to choose our emotional state, rather than being prey to unhelpful emotions, especially at times when we want to stay resourceful.

Observing self

A natural mechanism human beings have to step outside of our thoughts, feelings and actions and look in on ourselves, so that the world can be seen more objectively. It is a fundamental state of awareness which can be used by therapists to help a client identify the patterns of conditioning which need to change. The term was coined by the psychiatrist Dr Arthur Deikman.

Nocebo

Nocebo means 'I will harm'. The nocebo effect is the experience of negative health outcomes following a treatment that should have no effect.

Placebo

The literal meaning of placebo is 'I shall please'. The placebo effect has been much researched and refers to health benefits produced by treatments without demonstrable substance, and that should have no effect.

Psychoneuroimmunology

Following the discovery in 1974 by Robert Ader, a psychologist, that the immune system, like the brain, can learn, psychoneuroimmunology has become a leading-edge medical science, exploring the links between the mind and emotions, nervous system, hormone system and immune system.

Reframing

A core skill employed in counselling and psychotherapy, reframing addresses how a person 'frames' their experience. It is used to replace a negative, narrow, inaccurate or unhelpful way of interpreting their experience with a more hopeful, richer one that opens up new possibilities.

Stress response (Fight-or-flight response)

Originally discovered by the great Harvard physiologist Walter Cannon, this response is hard-wired into our brains to enable our physical survival in times of danger. The response corresponds to an area in the base of the brain called the hypothalamus, which, when stimulated by the amygdala, initiates a sequence of nerve cell firing and chemical release (including adrenaline, noradrenaline and cortisol) that prepares our body for running or fighting. In this survival mode, along with a series of physiological changes which occur, the rational mind is suppressed, and we are unable to think strategically, nor cultivate positive attitudes or beliefs.

USEFUL RESOURCES

Chapter 1: Lay the Foundations of Well-being: Some mind science basics

Relax CD with Piers Bishop by HG publishing, available at http://www.humangivens.com/publications/relax.html

Dyer W (2004) The Power Of Intention. Change the way you look at things and the things you look at will change. Hay House Inc.

Chapter 2: Deal with Stress, Anxiety, Panic and Worry

Griffin J and Tyrrell I (2007) How to Master Anxiety. Chalvington, UK: HG Publishing.

Chapter 3: Control Negative Thinking and Avoid Depression

Williams M, Teasdale J, Segal Z and Kabat-Zinn J (2007) The Mindful Way Through Depression. New York: Guilford Press.

www.clinical-depression.co.uk
Depression quiz, recovery programme and learning path available for people suffering from depression, those living with them, and therapists treating them.

Chapter 4: Reduce Anger

Dawes M and Winn D (1999) Managing The Monkey: How to diffuse the conflicts that can lead to violence in the workplace. Chalvington, UK: HG Publishing.

Griffin J and Tyrrell I (2008) *Release from Anger. Practical help for controlling unreasonable rage*. UK: HG Publishing.

Chapter 5: Improve Physical Health and Sleep
Cole F et al (2005) *Overcoming chronic pain: A self-help guide using cognitive behavioural techniques*. London: Constable & Robinson Ltd.

Espie C (2006) *Overcoming insomnia and sleep problems: A self-help guide using cognitive behavioural techniques*. London: Constable & Robinson Ltd.

Kabat-Zinn J (2004) *Full Catastrophe Living. How to cope with stress, pain and illness using mindfulness meditation*. London: Piatkus.

Mental Health Foundation (2011) *Sleep Well: Your Pocket Guide To Better Sleep*. London: Mental Health Foundation (free).

Chapter 6: Set Goals and Boost Your Motivation
Hadfield S (2012) *Brilliant Positive Thinking: Transform your outlook and face the future with confidence and optimism*. Harlow: Pearson Education Ltd.

Chapter 7: Enhance your Assertiveness, Self-esteem and Confidence
Robinson D (1997) *Too nice for your own good: How to stop making 9 self-sabotaging mistakes*. New York: Warner Books Inc.

Fennell M (2009) *Overcoming Low Self Esteem: A self help guide using Cognitive Behavioural Techniques*. London: Constable & Robinson Ltd.

Chapter 8: Improve Communication and Relationships
Beck A (1988) *Love is Never Enough. How couples can overcome misunderstandings,* resolve conflicts, and solve relationship problems through cognitive therapy. New York: Harper & Row.

Goleman D (1996) *Emotional Intelligence. Why it can matter more than IQ*. London: Bloomsbury Publishing.

Gottman J (1994) *Why Marriages Succeed or Fail and how you can make yours last*. New York: Simon & Schuster.

Chapter 9: Change Unhelpful Patterns
Goss K (2011) *The Compassionate Mind Approach to Beating Overeating. Using compassion focused therapy*. London: Constable.

Griffin J (2005) *Freedom from Addiction: The secret behind successful addiction busting*. Chalvington, UK: HG Publishing.

Prochaska J, Norcross J and DiClemente C (1994) *Changing For Good: The revolutionary program that explains the six stages of change and teaches you how to free yourself from bad habits*. New York: W. Morrow.

Chapter 10: Reach the Peak of Well-being
Buzan T (1988) *Make the Most of Your Mind*. London: Pan Books.

Seligman M (2003) *Authentic Happiness*. London: Nicholas Brealey Publishing.

www.authentichappiness.sas.upenn.edu/register.aspx
Develop insights into yourself and the world around you through these scientifically tested questionnaires, surveys, and scales.

Valliant G (2002) *Aging Well*. New York: Little, Brown.

GENERAL

Cognitive Behaviour Therapy
Beck Institute for Cognitive Behaviour Therapy
http://www.beckinstitute.org
An international training and resource centre
for health and mental health professionals,
educators, and students worldwide.

Carlson R (1997) *Stop Thinking and Start Living:
Common-sense strategies for discovering
lifelong happiness*. London: Element.

The MoodGYM http://moodgym.anu.edu.au
A free self-help program to teach cognitive
behavioural therapy skills to people vulnerable
to depression and anxiety.

Powell T (2009) *The Mental Health Handbook.
A cognitive behavioural approach*. Milton
Keynes: Speechmark Publishing.

Compassionate Mind approach
Gilbert P (2009) *The Compassionate Mind*.
London: Constable Robinson.
Compassionate Mind Foundation
www.compassionatemind.co.uk

Human Givens approach
Griffin J and Tyrrell I (2004) *Human Givens –
A new approach to emotional health and clear
thinking*. Chalvington, UK: HG Publishing.

Hypnotherapy
Alman B and Lambrou P (1992) *Self-Hypnosis.
The complete manual for health and self-
change (2nd edition)*. New York: Brunner/Mazel.

Erickson MH and Rossi EL (1979) *Hypnotherapy:
An Exploratory Casebook*. New York: Irvington.

Mindfulness
Kabat-Zinn J (2005) *Coming to our Senses:
Healing ourselves and the world through
mindfulness*. New York: Piatkus.

Siegel D (2007) *The Mindful Brain: Reflection
and attunement in the cultivation of well-being*.
London: W W Norton.

Neuro-Linguistic Programming
Bandler R and Grinder J (1979) *Frogs into
Princes: Neuro Linguistic Programming*. Moab,
UT: Real People Press.

O'Connor J (2001) *NLP Workbook. A practical
guide to achieving the results you want*.
London: Element.

Positive Psychology
Boniwell I (2008) *Positive Psychology in
a Nutshell (2nd ed)* London: Personal
Well-being Centre.

Other titles in the *49 Ways to Well-being
Series* include:

49 Ways to Eat Yourself Well
49 Ways to Write Yourself Well
49 Ways to Move Yourself Well
49 Ways to Mental Health Recovery
49 Ways to Sexual Well-being

For more details visit
www.stepbeachpress.co.uk/well-being